HOUGHTON MIFFLIN HARCOURT

MATH
Expressions
Common Core

Dr. Karen C. Fuson

GRADE
2

This material is based upon work supported by the
National Science Foundation
under Grant Numbers
ESI-9816320, REC-9806020, and RED-935373.

Any opinions, findings, and conclusions, or recommendations expressed in this material
are those of the author and do not necessarily reflect the views of the National Science Foundation.

 HOUGHTON MIFFLIN HARCOURT

Name _____

Homework

1. Write two equations for each Math Mountain.

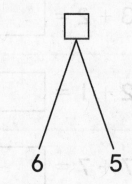

_____   _____   _____

_____   _____   _____

2. Draw a Math Mountain and write one more equation.

$5 + 8 = \square$ $17 - 8 = \square$ $7 + \square = 12$

_____   _____   _____

Remembering

Add.

1. $4 + 5 =$ ☐ $0 + 8 =$ ☐ $3 + 2 =$ ☐

2. $1 + 7 =$ ☐ $7 + 2 =$ ☐ $2 + 1 =$ ☐

3. $6 + 7 =$ ☐ $2 + 9 =$ ☐ $7 + 7 =$ ☐

4. $8 + 9 =$ ☐ $4 + 7 =$ ☐ $1 + 9 =$ ☐

Subtract.

5. $8 - 5 =$ ☐ $5 - 5 =$ ☐ $4 - 1 =$ ☐

6. $6 - 2 =$ ☐ $9 - 6 =$ ☐ $5 - 3 =$ ☐

7. $14 - 7 =$ ☐ $5 - 0 =$ ☐ $18 - 9 =$ ☐

8. $16 - 9 =$ ☐ $14 - 6 =$ ☐ $15 - 8 =$ ☐

9. **Stretch Your Thinking** The yard sale records got wet. Write the numbers that should be in the table.

Item	Number Sold Each Day		
	Saturday	Sunday	Total
Birdhouse	1	6	
Potholder	4		9
Picture Frame	2		10

Represent Addition and Subtraction

Homework

1. Complete the Math Mountains and equations.

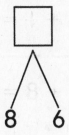 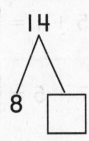 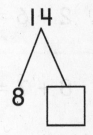

$8 + 6 = \boxed{}$ $8 + \boxed{} = 14$ $14 - 8 = \boxed{}$

2. Create and Solve Write and solve a word problem
for one of the equations above.

_____

_____

_____

_____

3. Draw a Picture and Explain Draw two different
Math Mountains with a total of 12. Explain why you
can make two different Math Mountains.

_____

_____

_____

Remembering

Add.

1. $2 + 6 =$ ☐ $5 + 1 =$ ☐ $8 + 1 =$ ☐

2. $8 + 7 =$ ☐ $7 + 5 =$ ☐ $8 + 8 =$ ☐

Subtract.

3. $9 - 3 =$ ☐ $4 - 2 =$ ☐ $8 - 1 =$ ☐

4. $12 - 8 =$ ☐ $16 - 9 =$ ☐ $15 - 8 =$ ☐

5. Write two equations for each Math Mountain.

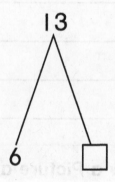

_____   _____   _____

_____   _____   _____

6. Stretch Your Thinking Write four equations for this Math Mountain.

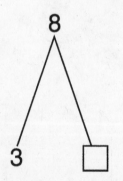

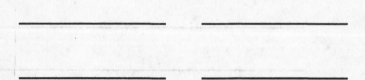

_____   _____

_____   _____

Name _____

Homework

Make a ten to find the total.

I. 3 + 8 = ☐   4 + 8 = ☐   4 + 9 = ☐

2. 8 + 6 = ☐   9 + 5 = ☐   8 + 5 = ☐

3. 6 + 7 = ☐   7 + 7 = ☐   7 + 5 = ☐

4. 2 + 9 = ☐   5 + 7 = ☐   9 + 2 = ☐

5. 3 + 9 = ☐   8 + 9 = ☐   4 + 7 = ☐

6. 9 + 8 = ☐   7 + 6 = ☐   5 + 9 = ☐

7. 6 + 9 = ☐   6 + 6 = ☐   5 + 6 = ☐

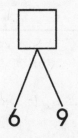   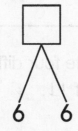   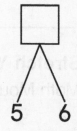

8. Critical Thinking Explain how to make a ten to find 8 + 6.

_____

_____

Name _____

Remembering

Add.

1.
$\begin{array}{r} 4 \\ + 7 \\ \hline \end{array}$
$\begin{array}{r} 5 \\ + 6 \\ \hline \end{array}$
$\begin{array}{r} 7 \\ + 8 \\ \hline \end{array}$
$\begin{array}{r} 8 \\ + 6 \\ \hline \end{array}$
$\begin{array}{r} 7 \\ + 7 \\ \hline \end{array}$
$\begin{array}{r} 9 \\ + 5 \\ \hline \end{array}$

Subtract.

2.
$\begin{array}{r} 13 \\ - 8 \\ \hline \end{array}$
$\begin{array}{r} 12 \\ - 7 \\ \hline \end{array}$
$\begin{array}{r} 17 \\ - 9 \\ \hline \end{array}$
$\begin{array}{r} 14 \\ - 6 \\ \hline \end{array}$
$\begin{array}{r} 15 \\ - 7 \\ \hline \end{array}$
$\begin{array}{r} 16 \\ - 8 \\ \hline \end{array}$

3. Write two equations for each Math Mountain.

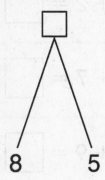

_____ _____ _____

_____ _____ _____

4. Stretch Your Thinking Write four different Math Mountains with a total of 11.

Make-a-Ten Strategies

$$8 + \boxed{6} = 14 \text{ or } 14 - 8 = \boxed{6}$$

Already   **8** $\overset{\bullet}{9} \ \overset{\bullet}{10} + 4 \text{ more}$

                    $\overset{\displaystyle 6}{\diagdown\!\diagup}$

or   **8** $+ 2 + 4 = 14$

or   **8** $\underset{10 \ + \ 4}{\bullet\bullet \ | \ \bullet\bullet\bullet\bullet}$

Already **8**

2 more to
10

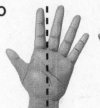

4 more to
14

Find the unknown addend (unknown partner).

1. $5 + \boxed{} = 12$ $15 - 8 = \boxed{}$ $8 + \boxed{} = 16$

2. $7 + \boxed{} = 16$ $13 - 4 = \boxed{}$ $9 + \boxed{} = 12$

3. $3 + \boxed{} = 12$ $11 - 2 = \boxed{}$ $7 + \boxed{} = 13$

4. $9 + \boxed{} = 15$ $14 - 8 = \boxed{}$ $17 - 9 = \boxed{}$

5. $8 + \boxed{} = 12$ $16 - 8 = \boxed{}$ $16 - 7 = \boxed{}$

6. $5 + \boxed{} = 13$ $18 - 9 = \boxed{}$ $12 - 7 = \boxed{}$

7. $4 + \boxed{} = 12$ $11 - 4 = \boxed{}$ $12 - 9 = \boxed{}$

8. Explain Your Thinking Choose one equation above.
Explain how you can make a ten to find the partner.

Remembering

Add.

1.   6   7   8   9   6   5
   + 9   + 6   + 8   + 7   + 8   + 8

Subtract.

2.   11   15   18   13   16   14
   − 3   − 8   − 9   − 4   − 9   − 7

3. Complete the Math Mountains and equations.

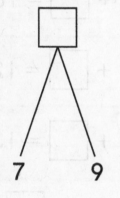
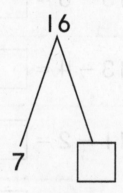
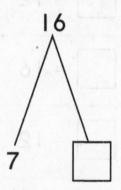

$7 + 9 = \boxed{}$ $7 + \boxed{} = 16$ $16 - 7 = \boxed{}$

Make a ten to find the total.

4. $4 + 8 = \boxed{}$ $8 + 9 = \boxed{}$ $8 + 8 = \boxed{}$

5. Stretch Your Thinking Which problem is easiest to
solve using the make-a-ten strategy? Explain why.

$4 + 5 = \boxed{}$ $6 + 5 = \boxed{}$ $9 + 5 = \boxed{}$

_____

_____

Name _____

Homework

Write the unknown addend (partner).

1. $6 + \boxed{} = 15$ $17 - 8 = \boxed{}$ $3 + \boxed{} = 11$

2. $9 + \boxed{} = 17$ $12 - 6 = \boxed{}$ $9 + \boxed{} = 12$

3. $5 + \boxed{} = 11$ $12 - 4 = \boxed{}$ $7 + \boxed{} = 12$

4. $8 + \boxed{} = 13$ $15 - 7 = \boxed{}$ $5 + \boxed{} = 14$

5. $7 + \boxed{} = 11$ $15 - 8 = \boxed{}$ $13 - 7 = \boxed{}$

6. $9 + \boxed{} = 14$ $13 - 5 = \boxed{}$ $11 - 6 = \boxed{}$

7. $5 + \boxed{} = 12$ $12 - 3 = \boxed{}$ $11 - 2 = \boxed{}$

8. $8 + \boxed{} = 13$ $15 - 9 = \boxed{}$ $13 - 6 = \boxed{}$

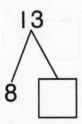
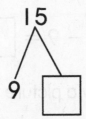
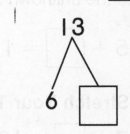

9. Critical Thinking Explain how the math
drawing can help you solve $8 + \boxed{} = 14$.

Already 8 $\begin{array}{c} \bullet\bullet \,|\, \bullet\bullet\bullet\bullet \\ 10 + 4 = 14 \end{array}$

_____

_____

More Practice with Unknown Addends and Teen Totals **9**

Remembering

Add.

1.
```
   8        6        7        7        6        8
 + 5      + 5      + 7      + 8      + 7      + 9
 ___      ___      ___      ___      ___      ___
```

Subtract.

2.
```
  16       15       18       12       11       13
 - 8      - 9      - 9      - 8      - 7      - 5
 ___      ___      ___      ___      ___      ___
```

3. Complete the Math Mountains and equations.

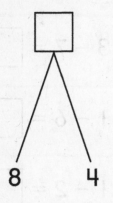   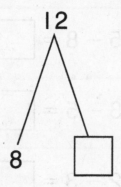   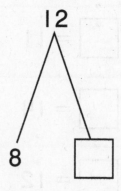

$8 + 4 = \boxed{}$ $8 + \boxed{} = 12$ $12 - 8 = \boxed{}$

Find the unknown addend (unknown partner).

4. $5 + \boxed{} = 11$ $13 - 9 = \boxed{}$ $5 + \boxed{} = 13$

5. **Stretch Your Thinking** Draw a picture to help you solve

$7 + \boxed{} = 12.$

More Practice with Unknown Addends and Teen Totals

Homework

Draw lines to make pairs.
Write odd or even.

1. ● ● ●
   ● ● ● ●

2. ● ● ● ● ● ● ●
   ● ● ● ● ● ● ●

_____

3. ● ● ● ●
   ● ● ● ●

4. ● ● ● ● ● ●
   ● ● ● ● ● ● ●

_____   _____

Complete the addition doubles equation.

5. ☐ + ☐ = 18

6. ☐ + ☐ = 6

7. ☐ + ☐ = 10

8. ☐ + ☐ = 4

9. ☐ + ☐ = 8

10. ☐ + ☐ = 14

11. ☐ + ☐ = 16

12. ☐ + ☐ = 12

Remembering

Add.

1.   7   6   9   7   6   3
    + 8   + 5   + 2   + 5   + 8   + 8
    ____   ____   ____   ____   ____   ____

Subtract.

2.   13   15   17   16   18   11
    − 4   − 8   − 9   − 7   − 9   − 3
    ____   ____   ____   ____   ____   ____

3. Draw a Math Mountain and write one more equation.

$9 + 6 = \square$ $4 + 6 = \square$ $8 + 7 = \square$

_____   _____   _____

Make a ten to find the total.

4. $5 + 8 = \boxed{}$ $8 + 4 = \boxed{}$ $5 + 6 = \boxed{}$

5. **Stretch Your Thinking** Draw a Math Mountain
   that only uses two different numbers. Explain why.

_____

_____

Odd and Even Numbers

Homework

Name _____

Add. Use doubles.

1. $7 + 5 =$ ☐ $7 + 7 =$ ☐ $8 + 9 =$ ☐

2. $9 + 9 =$ ☐ $9 + 11 =$ ☐ $8 + 8 =$ ☐

3. $8 + 7 =$ ☐ $6 + 5 =$ ☐ $7 + 8 =$ ☐

4. $6 + 4 =$ ☐ $7 + 9 =$ ☐ $9 + 7 =$ ☐

5. $7 + 6 =$ ☐ $5 + 5 =$ ☐ $6 + 8 =$ ☐

6. $6 + 6 =$ ☐ $6 + 7 =$ ☐ $8 + 6 =$ ☐

7. $8 + 10 =$ ☐ $5 + 6 =$ ☐ $9 + 10 =$ ☐

8. $9 + 8 =$ ☐ $10 + 9 =$ ☐ $5 + 7 =$ ☐

Remembering

Add.

1.

4	8	7	9	6	8
+ 5	+ 3	+ 8	+ 0	+ 9	+ 5

Subtract.

2.

14	11	18	10	7	15
− 6	− 5	− 9	− 5	− 5	− 6

3. Complete the Math Mountains and equations.

6 + 8 = ☐

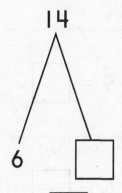

6 + ☐ = 14

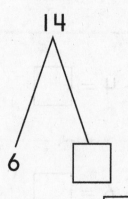

14 − 6 = ☐

Write the unknown addend (partner).

4. 6 + ☐ = 12   15 − 7 = ☐   7 + ☐ = 16

5. Stretch Your Thinking You have a stack of pennies.
Without counting the pennies, how can you know if
there is an odd or even number of them?

_____

_____

_____

Strategies Using Doubles

Homework

$9 + 4 = \boxed{13}$

$\boxed{13}$

9
9   4

I find the total.

$\begin{array}{r} 9 \\ + 4 \\ \hline 13 \end{array}$

$13 - 9 = \boxed{4}$

13

9    $\boxed{4}$

I find a partner.

$\begin{array}{r} 13 \\ - 9 \\ \hline 4 \end{array}$

Find the total or partner.

1.
$\begin{array}{r} 5 \\ + 6 \\ \hline \end{array}$
$\begin{array}{r} 9 \\ + 8 \\ \hline \end{array}$
$\begin{array}{r} 8 \\ + 3 \\ \hline \end{array}$
$\begin{array}{r} 9 \\ + 4 \\ \hline \end{array}$
$\begin{array}{r} 6 \\ + 6 \\ \hline \end{array}$
$\begin{array}{r} 8 \\ + 6 \\ \hline \end{array}$

2.
$\begin{array}{r} 11 \\ - 9 \\ \hline \end{array}$
$\begin{array}{r} 14 \\ - 6 \\ \hline \end{array}$
$\begin{array}{r} 11 \\ - 4 \\ \hline \end{array}$
$\begin{array}{r} 13 \\ - 5 \\ \hline \end{array}$
$\begin{array}{r} 12 \\ - 3 \\ \hline \end{array}$
$\begin{array}{r} 16 \\ - 9 \\ \hline \end{array}$

3.
$\begin{array}{r} 16 \\ - 8 \\ \hline \end{array}$
$\begin{array}{r} 15 \\ - 7 \\ \hline \end{array}$
$\begin{array}{r} 12 \\ - 5 \\ \hline \end{array}$
$\begin{array}{r} 11 \\ - 2 \\ \hline \end{array}$
$\begin{array}{r} 17 \\ - 9 \\ \hline \end{array}$
$\begin{array}{r} 14 \\ - 7 \\ \hline \end{array}$

4. Draw a Math Mountain to solve.

$16 - 7 = \boxed{}$

Remembering

Add.

1.
$$\begin{array}{r} 4 \\ + 9 \\ \hline \end{array} \qquad \begin{array}{r} 8 \\ + 8 \\ \hline \end{array} \qquad \begin{array}{r} 9 \\ + 8 \\ \hline \end{array} \qquad \begin{array}{r} 7 \\ + 2 \\ \hline \end{array} \qquad \begin{array}{r} 8 \\ + 9 \\ \hline \end{array} \qquad \begin{array}{r} 5 \\ + 9 \\ \hline \end{array}$$

Subtract.

2.
$$\begin{array}{r} 15 \\ - 8 \\ \hline \end{array} \qquad \begin{array}{r} 11 \\ - 3 \\ \hline \end{array} \qquad \begin{array}{r} 16 \\ - 7 \\ \hline \end{array} \qquad \begin{array}{r} 9 \\ - 6 \\ \hline \end{array} \qquad \begin{array}{r} 14 \\ - 8 \\ \hline \end{array} \qquad \begin{array}{r} 8 \\ - 8 \\ \hline \end{array}$$

3. Draw a Math Mountain and write one more equation.

$5 + 6 = \boxed{}$ $\qquad$ $9 + 7 = \boxed{}$ $\qquad$ $8 + 4 = \boxed{}$

_____ $\qquad$ _____ $\qquad$ _____

Complete the addition doubles equation.

4. $\boxed{} + \boxed{} = 18$ $\qquad$ 5. $\boxed{} + \boxed{} = 12$

6. **Stretch Your Thinking** Suppose you cannot remember the

answer to $15 - 8 = \boxed{}$. What could you do to solve?

_____

_____

Name _____

Homework

Add in any order. Write the total.

1. $9 + 1 + 4 =$ ☐

2. $6 + 9 + 1 =$ ☐

3. $8 + 9 + 1 =$ ☐

4. $7 + 8 + 2 =$ ☐

5. $7 + 5 + 3 =$ ☐

6. $8 + 8 + 2 =$ ☐

7. $1 + 4 + 8 =$ ☐

8. $5 + 6 + 7 =$ ☐

9. $4 + 3 + 8 =$ ☐

10. $2 + 7 + 6 =$ ☐

11. $9 + 9 + 2 =$ ☐

12. $6 + 3 + 7 =$ ☐

13. $4 + 3 + 2 + 4 =$ ☐

14. $6 + 4 + 5 + 5 =$ ☐

15. $8 + 3 + 1 + 7 =$ ☐

16. $1 + 7 + 2 + 4 =$ ☐

17. $3 + 7 + 9 + 3 =$ ☐

18. $7 + 6 + 3 + 4 =$ ☐

19. $8 + 3 + 9 + 3 =$ ☐

20. $1 + 8 + 9 + 4 =$ ☐

Remembering

Add.

1.
```
   7        8        9        4        3        5
 + 9      + 5      + 6      + 2      + 9      + 1
```

Subtract.

2.
```
  17       12       13        5       11       18
 - 8      - 5      - 7      - 5      - 2      - 9
```

Make a ten to find the total.

3. $9 + 6 = \square$ $8 + 8 = \square$ $8 + 3 = \square$

4. $5 + 7 = \square$ $6 + 8 = \square$ $4 + 9 = \square$

Find the total or partner.

5.
```
   4        8        9        5        4        6
 + 8      + 7      + 5      + 6      + 4      + 9
```

6.
```
  16       11       14       15       11       13
 - 9      - 5      - 7      - 9      - 4      - 9
```

7. **Stretch Your Thinking** Explain a way you could
   add $3 + 4 + 7 + 6$.

_____

_____

Add Three or Four Addends

Homework

Make a drawing. Write an equation.
Solve the problem.

Show your work.

1. Brad has 14 toy boats. 5 of them float
   away. How many does he have now?

boat

☐ _____
       label

2. Moses collects 17 rocks. He gives some
   of them away. Now he has 9 rocks left.
   How many does he give away?

rock

☐ _____
       label

3. Claire has 9 markers in her backpack.
   Some fall out on the way home. Now she
   has only 5 markers. How many markers
   fall out of her backpack?

backpack

☐ _____
       label

4. A honeybee visits 7 flowers in the garden.
   Then it visits 5 more. How many flowers
   does the honeybee visit in all?

honeybee

☐ _____
       label

Add To and *Take From* Word Problems **19**

Remembering

1. Write two equations for each Math Mountain.

_____   _____

_____   _____

Write the unknown addend (partner).

2. $5 + \boxed{} = 11$ $13 - 8 = \boxed{}$ $15 - 6 = \boxed{}$

Add in any order. Write the total.

3. $5 + 3 + 5 = \boxed{}$ $7 + 8 + 3 = \boxed{}$ $2 + 9 + 7 = \boxed{}$

4. $8 + 2 + 3 + 4 = \boxed{}$ $2 + 6 + 6 + 8 = \boxed{}$

5. Stretch Your Thinking Write a word
problem to match this drawing.

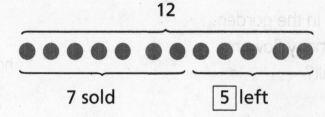

12

7 sold $\boxed{5}$ left

_____

     Add To and *Take From* Word Problems

Make a drawing. Write an equation.
Solve the problem.

Show your work.

1. In the morning, Nick makes 8 animals out of clay. In the afternoon, he makes some more clay animals. Altogether, he makes 15 clay animals. How many did he make in the afternoon?

clay animal

☐ _____
    label

2. Carrie sees some birds in a tree. 8 fly away. 5 are left. How many birds were in the tree in the beginning?

bird

☐ _____
    label

3. Leon and his friends made 12 snowmen. The next day, Leon sees that some of them have melted. Only 9 snowmen are left. How many melted?

snowmen

☐ _____
    label

4. 3 lizards sit on a rock in the sun. Then 9 more come out and sit on the rock. How many lizards are on the rock now?

rock

☐ _____
    label

| **Name** _____

Remembering

Add. Use doubles.

1. $8 + 6 =$ ☐ $\qquad$ $7 + 8 =$ ☐ $\qquad$ $5 + 6 =$ ☐

2. $7 + 6 =$ ☐ $\qquad$ $11 + 9 =$ ☐ $\qquad$ $8 + 9 =$ ☐

3. Complete the Math Mountains and equations.

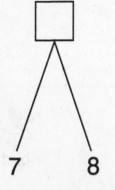 $\qquad$ 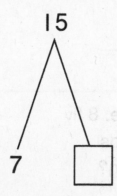 $\qquad$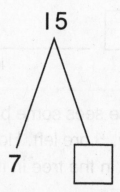

$7 + 8 =$ ☐ $\qquad$ $7 +$ ☐ $= 15$ $\qquad$ $15 - 7 =$ ☐

Make a ten to find the total.

4. $5 + 9 =$ ☐ $\qquad$ $5 + 8 =$ ☐ $\qquad$ $3 + 9 =$ ☐

5. $8 + 6 =$ ☐ $\qquad$ $4 + 7 =$ ☐ $\qquad$ $9 + 7 =$ ☐

6. **Stretch Your Thinking** Write a word problem to match this drawing.

6 now $\quad$ 7 $\quad$ 8 $\quad$ 9 $\quad$ 10 $\quad$ 11 $\quad$ 11 to start

_____

_____

$\qquad$ *Add To* and *Take From* Problems-Unknown in All Positions

Homework

Make a drawing. Write an equation.
Solve the problem.

Show your work.

---

1. There are some pigs on Mr. Smith's farm. 8 of them are eating corn. The other 7 are drinking water. How many pigs are on Mr. Smith's farm?

pig

☐ _____
       label

---

2. Wendy buys 3 blue balloons and some red balloons for a party. She buys 11 balloons. How many red balloons does she buy?

balloon

☐ _____
       label

---

3. There are 14 children at the park. 7 of them are on the swings. The rest are jumping rope. How many are jumping rope?

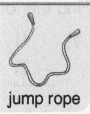
jump rope

☐ _____
       label

---

4. Sean buys 9 red tomatoes and 6 green tomatoes. How many tomatoes does he buy?

tomato

☐ _____
       label

Remembering

Draw lines to make pairs. Write odd or even.

1. ● ● ● ●
   ● ● ● ● ●

   _____

2. ● ● ● ● ● ● ● ●
   ● ● ● ● ● ● ●

   _____

3. ● ● ● ● ● ● ●
   ● ● ● ● ● ● ● ● ●

   _____

4. ● ● ● ● ● ●
   ● ● ● ● ● ●

   _____

Add. Use doubles.

5. $7 + 8 =$ ☐ $9 + 8 =$ ☐ $5 + 4 =$ ☐

6. $8 + 6 =$ ☐ $5 + 3 =$ ☐ $6 + 7 =$ ☐

Find the total or partner.

7.
$$\begin{array}{r} 4 \\ + 8 \\ \hline \end{array} \qquad \begin{array}{r} 5 \\ + 8 \\ \hline \end{array} \qquad \begin{array}{r} 9 \\ + 9 \\ \hline \end{array} \qquad \begin{array}{r} 7 \\ + 6 \\ \hline \end{array} \qquad \begin{array}{r} 3 \\ + 9 \\ \hline \end{array} \qquad \begin{array}{r} 2 \\ + 9 \\ \hline \end{array}$$

8.
$$\begin{array}{r} 16 \\ - 8 \\ \hline \end{array} \qquad \begin{array}{r} 12 \\ - 3 \\ \hline \end{array} \qquad \begin{array}{r} 15 \\ - 7 \\ \hline \end{array} \qquad \begin{array}{r} 14 \\ - 5 \\ \hline \end{array} \qquad \begin{array}{r} 12 \\ - 7 \\ \hline \end{array} \qquad \begin{array}{r} 8 \\ - 2 \\ \hline \end{array}$$

9. **Stretch Your Thinking** Write a word problem that
   uses doubles and solve.

   _____

   _____

Put Together / Take Apart Problems

Homework

Make a drawing. Write an equation. Solve the problem.

Show your work.

---

1. One bus has 6 girls and 7 boys on it.
How many children are on the bus?

☐ _____
     label

bus

---

2. Pang buys some oranges. Bill buys
6 pears. Pang and Bill buy 13 pieces
of fruit. How many oranges does Pang buy?

☐ _____
     label

orange

---

3. Davant has 16 birds. He has 7 parrots.
The rest are canaries. How many
canaries does Davant have?

☐ _____
     label

canary

---

4. Complete the diagram by adding at
least two things in the circle.
Write the group name.

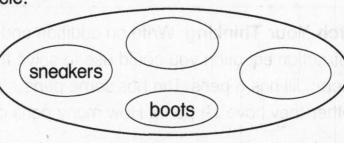

sneakers

boots

_____
Group Name

Remembering

Make a ten to find the total.

1. $9 + 5 = \boxed{}$ $\qquad$ $4 + 9 = \boxed{}$ $\qquad$ $8 + 5 = \boxed{}$

2. $8 + 6 = \boxed{}$ $\qquad$ $7 + 7 = \boxed{}$ $\qquad$ $4 + 8 = \boxed{}$

Find the unknown addend (unknown partner).

3. $7 + \boxed{} = 13$ $\qquad$ $17 - 8 = \boxed{}$ $\qquad$ $9 - 7 = \boxed{}$

Make a drawing. Write an equation. Solve the problem. $\qquad$ **Show your work.**

4. Jim has a box of crayons. He pulls out
8 crayons. 7 are left. How many crayons
were in the box to start?

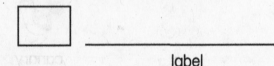

$\qquad$ label

5. Tanya has 9 tulips in a vase. She adds
5 more tulips to the vase. How many
tulips are in the vase now?

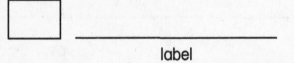

$\qquad$ label

6. Stretch Your Thinking Write an addition and
a subtraction equation you could use to solve this
problem: Jill has 6 pens. Ian has some pens.
Together they have 14 pens. How many pens does Ian have?

_____ _____

Homework

Make a matching drawing or draw comparison bars.
Solve the problem.

Show your work.

1. Peter has 13 eggs. Joe has 4 fewer eggs than
   Peter. How many eggs does Joe have?

eggs

_____
label

2. I want to give each of my 14 friends an
   apple. I have 8 apples in my basket.
   How many more apples do I need to
   pick to give each friend an apple?

basket

_____
label

3. Lë has 5 lemons. Tina has 7 more lemons
   than Lë. How many lemons does Tina have?

lemon

_____
label

Write Your Own Complete this word problem.
Draw comparison bars and solve.

4. I have 12 _____.

   My friend has _____ fewer

   _____ than I have. How many

   _____ does my friend have?

_____
label

Remembering

1. Complete the Math Mountains and equations.

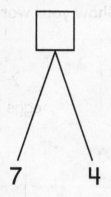

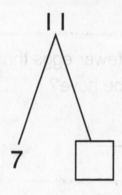

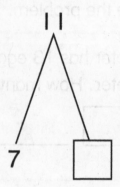

$7 + 4 = \boxed{}$

$7 + \boxed{} = 11$

$11 - 7 = \boxed{}$

Find the unknown addend (unknown partner).

2. $7 + \boxed{} = 15$ $13 - \boxed{} = 5$ $9 + \boxed{} = 15$

3. $3 + \boxed{} = 9$ $13 - \boxed{} = 6$ $8 + \boxed{} = 11$

Make a drawing. Write an equation.
Solve the problem.   **Show your work.**

4. A table has 16 glasses on it. 7 of the
glasses are large. The rest are small.
How many glasses are small?

$\boxed{}$ _____
          label

5. Stretch Your Thinking Write a word problem to
match this comparison bar drawing and solve.

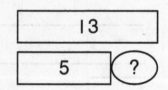

_____

_____

Compare Word Problems

Name _____

Homework

Make a drawing. Write an equation.
Solve the problem.

Show your work.

---

1. Parker and Natu go to the store to buy sunglasses. Parker pays $9 for his sunglasses. Natu pays $6 more than Parker. How much does Natu pay for his sunglasses?

sunglasses

☐ _____

label

---

2. A small ball costs 8 cents. A ring costs 8 more cents than the small ball. How many cents does a ring cost?

ring

☐ _____

label

---

3. If Jared gives away 4 strawberries, he will have as many strawberries as Phil. Jared has 11 strawberries. How many strawberries does Phil have?

strawberries

☐ _____

label

---

4. Andrew has 11 soccer balls. William has 3 soccer balls. How many fewer soccer balls does William have than Andrew?

soccer ball

☐ _____

label

More *Compare* Word Problems **29**

Remembering

Add.

1.
$$\begin{array}{r} 5 \\ +\,6 \\ \hline \end{array} \qquad \begin{array}{r} 9 \\ +\,3 \\ \hline \end{array} \qquad \begin{array}{r} 8 \\ +\,3 \\ \hline \end{array} \qquad \begin{array}{r} 2 \\ +\,9 \\ \hline \end{array} \qquad \begin{array}{r} 6 \\ +\,6 \\ \hline \end{array} \qquad \begin{array}{r} 8 \\ +\,6 \\ \hline \end{array}$$

Make a drawing. Write an equation.   **Show your work.**
Solve the problem.

2. Jamie has some grapes on her plate.
Tom has 9 grapes. Together, Jamie and
Tom have 14 grapes. How many grapes
does Jamie have?

☐ _____
         label

3. Complete the diagram by adding at least two
things in the circle. Write the group name.

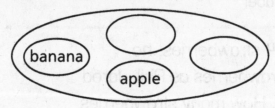

_____
       Group Name

4. Stretch Your Thinking Write a word problem
that would have the top comparison bar
with a question mark in it. Then solve using a
comparison bar drawing.

_____

_____

     More *Compare* Word Problems

Homework

Make a drawing. Write an equation.
Solve the problem.

Show your work.

---

1. Susan rides her bicycle for 14 blocks. Awan rides his bicycle for 8 blocks. How many fewer blocks does Awan ride than Susan?

bicycle

☐ _____
    label

---

2. Eden has 7 blackberries. Her father gives her 9 more. How many blackberries does Eden have now?

blackberries

☐ _____
    label

---

3. There were 9 children on the bus. At the first bus stop, some children get off. 7 children are still on the bus. How many children got off at the first bus stop?

bus stop

☐ _____
    label

---

4. The clown has 12 red balloons. He has 4 blue balloons. How many more red balloons than blue balloons does he have?

balloons

☐ _____
    label

Remembering

1. Draw a Math Mountain and write one more equation.

$8 + 9 = \square$　　　$6 + 7 = \square$　　　$5 + 8 = \square$

_____　　_____　　_____

Complete the addition doubles equation.

2. $\square + \square = 12$　　　　$\square + \square = 18$

Find the total or partner.

3.
$$\begin{array}{r} 3 \\ + 7 \\ \hline \end{array} \qquad \begin{array}{r} 6 \\ + 8 \\ \hline \end{array} \qquad \begin{array}{r} 8 \\ + 9 \\ \hline \end{array} \qquad \begin{array}{r} 7 \\ + 7 \\ \hline \end{array} \qquad \begin{array}{r} 1 \\ + 9 \\ \hline \end{array} \qquad \begin{array}{r} 4 \\ + 9 \\ \hline \end{array}$$

4.
$$\begin{array}{r} 16 \\ - 9 \\ \hline \end{array} \qquad \begin{array}{r} 14 \\ - 5 \\ \hline \end{array} \qquad \begin{array}{r} 13 \\ - 7 \\ \hline \end{array} \qquad \begin{array}{r} 16 \\ - 8 \\ \hline \end{array} \qquad \begin{array}{r} 12 \\ - 4 \\ \hline \end{array} \qquad \begin{array}{r} 9 \\ - 5 \\ \hline \end{array}$$

5. Stretch Your Thinking Write a word problem
that you could use a Math Mountain drawing
to solve. Then solve it.

_____

_____

Homework

Cross out the extra information or write hidden or
missing information. Then solve the problem.

Show your work.

---

1. Joel has 9 dinosaur cards and 8 bird cards.
His friend Peja has 6 dinosaur cards. How
many dinosaur cards do the two friends
have altogether?

dinosaur

_____

☐ _____
　　　label

---

2. I have a ring for each finger of both hands.
I want to buy 4 more rings. How many rings
will I have then?

hands

_____

☐ _____
　　　label

---

3. Erica had 6 coins in her coin collection.
She goes to a coin show and buys
some more coins. How many coins
does she have now?

coin

_____

☐ _____
　　　label

Remembering

Add in any order. Write the total.

1. $7 + 3 + 5 = \boxed{}$ $8 + 4 + 8 = \boxed{}$

2. $4 + 2 + 8 = \boxed{}$ $1 + 6 + 9 = \boxed{}$

3. $6 + 2 + 4 + 4 = \boxed{}$ $2 + 6 + 4 + 8 = \boxed{}$

Make a drawing. Write an equation.   **Show your work.**
Solve the problem.

4. Ryan has 8 stickers. His friend gives
him 7 more. How many stickers does
Ryan have now?

$\boxed{}$ _____
label

5. The top shelf has a display of 12 pictures.
The bottom shelf has 7 pictures. How
many fewer pictures are on the bottom
shelf than are on the top shelf?

$\boxed{}$ _____
label

6. Stretch Your Thinking Why can a problem
with extra information be difficult to solve?

_____

_____

Homework

Draw comparison bars. Write an equation.
Solve the problem.

Show your work.

bird

1. Morgan sees 15 birds on a bird-watching
trip. She sees 6 more birds than Shari.
How many birds does Shari see?

[ ] _____
label

parking lot

2. There are 5 fewer trucks than cars in the
parking lot. If there are 8 trucks, how
many cars are there?

[ ] _____
label

quilt

3. Anh makes 12 quilts. Krista makes 7 fewer
quilts than Anh. How many quilts does
Krista make?

[ ] _____
label

lion

4. There are 8 fewer tigers than lions at the
zoo. There are 8 tigers at the zoo. How
many lions does the zoo have?

[ ] _____
label

Name

Remembering

Find the unknown addend (unknown partner).

1. 3 + ☐ = 12   14 − ☐ = 8   15 − 6 = ☐

2. 4 + ☐ = 13   15 − ☐ = 7   14 − 7 = ☐

Solve the word problems.   **Show your work.**

3. There are 13 dancers in the
   front row. 7 dancers are in the
   back row. How many fewer
   dancers are in the back row than
   are in the front row?

   ☐ _____
            label

4. There are 8 birds in the red cage.
   The blue cage has 4 more birds
   than the red cage. How many birds
   are in the blue cage?

   ☐ _____
            label

5. **Stretch Your Thinking** When would you use
   a drawing of comparison bars for a word problem?

   _____

   _____

   _____

More Complex *Compare* Problems

Homework

Think about the first-step question. Then
solve the problem.

Show your work.

1. Bessie counts 5 fish, 3 turtles,
   and some frogs. She counts
   14 animals altogether. How
   many frogs does Bessie count?

turtle

[ ] _____

   label

2. Amy has 6 more blue feathers
   than white feathers. She has
   2 more green feathers than blue
   feathers. Amy has 4 white feathers.
   How many green feathers does
   Amy have?

feather

[ ] _____

   label

3. Mr. Green puts 5 tulips and
   some roses in a vase. There
   are 14 flowers in the vase.
   Then Mrs. Green adds 2 more
   roses to the vase. How many
   roses are in the vase now?

vase

[ ] _____

   label

Remembering

Subtract.

1. 17   14   16   15   11   14
   − 9   − 6   − 7   − 8   − 6   − 8
  _____   _____   _____   _____   _____   _____

Add. Use doubles.

2. 4 + 3 = ☐   7 + 8 = ☐   6 + 4 = ☐

3. 7 + 6 = ☐   5 + 7 = ☐   8 + 9 = ☐

Make a drawing. Write an equation. Solve the problem.   **Show your work.**

4. Tom has 12 coins. 9 of them are quarters.
   The rest are pennies. How many pennies
   does Tom have?

   ☐ _____
            label

5. Erica has 15 stickers. Sharon has
   9 stickers. How many fewer stickers
   does Sharon have than Erica?

   ☐ _____
            label

6. **Stretch Your Thinking** Are all two-step word
   problems solved the same way? Explain.

   _____

   _____

       Two-Step Word Problems

Homework

Make a drawing. Write an equation.
Solve the problem.

Show your work.

1. Malia has 8 hamsters. That is 6 fewer than
   Sasha has. How many hamsters does
   Sasha have?

   hamster

   ☐ _____
           label

2. Han brings some sandwiches to a picnic.
   He gives 6 sandwiches to his friends.
   Now he has 6 sandwiches left. How many
   sandwiches did Han bring to the picnic?

   sandwich

   ☐ _____
           label

3. 15 children are playing marbles.
   9 are boys and the rest are girls. Then
   5 more girls join them. How many
   girls are playing marbles now?

   marbles

   ☐ _____
           label

4. Mike and 3 friends go to the theater.
   There are 9 other children at the
   theater. How many children are at
   the theater altogether?

   theater

   ☐ _____
           label

Remembering

Make a ten to find the total.

1. $8 + 7 = \boxed{}$ $2 + 9 = \boxed{}$ $7 + 5 = \boxed{}$

2. $7 + 4 = \boxed{}$ $3 + 8 = \boxed{}$ $8 + 4 = \boxed{}$

Add in any order. Write the total.

3. $5 + 3 + 7 = \boxed{}$ $9 + 8 + 1 = \boxed{}$

4. $5 + 4 + 5 + 2 = \boxed{}$ $8 + 2 + 9 + 4 = \boxed{}$

Find the total or partner.

5.

5	6	7	6	8	2
$+\,7$	$+\,9$	$+\,9$	$+\,6$	$+\,4$	$+\,9$

6.

11	17	14	15	12	16
$-\,4$	$-\,9$	$-\,8$	$-\,8$	$-\,3$	$-\,9$

7. Stretch Your Thinking Write a problem that
can be solved with addition or subtraction.
Then solve it.

_____

_____

_____

_____

Mrs. Wise and her three children went to the apple orchard.
The table shows the number of apples each picked.

Apples Picked

Name	Number
Mrs. Wise	6
Michelle	4
George	3
Jen	4

Use the table to solve each story problem.   **Show your work.**

---

1. What was the total number of apples they picked?

☐ _____
           label

---

2. Two children picked the same number of apples.
Who were the children?

_____

How many apples did those two children pick in all?

☐ _____
           label

---

3. Use the information in the table to write your own
problem. Solve the problem.

_____

☐ _____
           label

Name _____

Remembering

1. Write two equations for each Math Mountain.

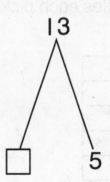

_____   _____   _____

_____   _____   _____

Write the unknown addend (partner).

2. $6 + \boxed{} = 11$ $18 - 9 = \boxed{}$ $5 + \boxed{} = 13$

Solve the word problem.   **Show your work.**

3. Don has 5 more pencils than crayons. He has 3 more markers than pencils. Don has 7 crayons. How many markers does Don have?

  _____
　　　　label

4. Stretch Your Thinking Fifteen children voted for their favorite color. The votes for red and blue together were double the votes for green and yellow together. How did the children vote?

Favorite Color Votes	
Color	**Votes**
Red	
Blue	
Green	
Yellow	

_____

Focus on Mathematical Practices

Homework

1. Write the numbers going down to see the tens.

1	11			41			71		
2									92
3						63			
				44			74		
	25								95
					56				
			37						
	18							88	
						69			
10	20			50					100

2. What number comes after 100? _____

3. What number comes next? _____

Remembering

1. Complete the Math Mountains and equations.

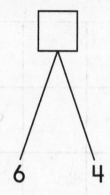
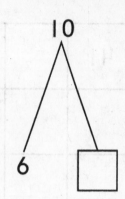
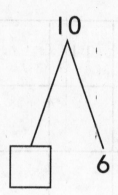

$6 + 4 = \boxed{}$ $6 + \boxed{} = 10$ $10 - 6 = \boxed{}$

Make a ten to find the total.

2. $5 + 7 = \boxed{}$ $8 + 5 = \boxed{}$ $4 + 9 = \boxed{}$

3. $2 + 9 = \boxed{}$ $3 + 8 = \boxed{}$ $6 + 8 = \boxed{}$

4. $7 + 9 = \boxed{}$ $5 + 6 = \boxed{}$ $4 + 8 = \boxed{}$

5. $9 + 9 = \boxed{}$ $7 + 6 = \boxed{}$ $6 + 6 = \boxed{}$

6. Stretch Your Thinking Add 2 tens to 100. What is the number? Explain your thinking.

_____

© Houghton Mifflin Harcourt Publishing Company

Ones, Tens, and Hundreds

Add.

1. $50 + 40 =$ _____ $80 + 10 =$ _____ $60 + 20 =$ _____

   $5 + 4 =$ _____ $8 + 1 =$ _____ $6 + 2 =$ _____

2. $10 + 70 =$ _____ $30 + 70 =$ _____ $40 + 30 =$ _____

   $1 + 7 =$ _____ $3 + 7 =$ _____ $4 + 3 =$ _____

3. $30 + 60 =$ _____ $20 + 80 =$ _____ $50 + 40 =$ _____

   $3 + 6 =$ _____ $2 + 8 =$ _____ $5 + 4 =$ _____

4. $50 + 30 =$ _____ $70 + 20 =$ _____ $40 + 60 =$ _____

   $5 + 3 =$ _____ $7 + 2 =$ _____ $4 + 6 =$ _____

5. $90 + 10 =$ _____ $50 + 20 =$ _____ $20 + 30 =$ _____

   $9 + 1 =$ _____ $5 + 2 =$ _____ $2 + 3 =$ _____

6. $30 + 10 =$ _____ $50 + 30 =$ _____ $40 + 20 =$ _____

   $3 + 1 =$ _____ $5 + 3 =$ _____ $4 + 2 =$ _____

Remembering

Make a ten to find the total.

1. $8 + 4 = \boxed{}$ $5 + 9 = \boxed{}$ $6 + 8 = \boxed{}$

2. $5 + 9 = \boxed{}$ $6 + 7 = \boxed{}$ $3 + 8 = \boxed{}$

3. $2 + 9 = \boxed{}$ $7 + 5 = \boxed{}$ $6 + 9 = \boxed{}$

4. $9 + 9 = \boxed{}$ $4 + 8 = \boxed{}$ $8 + 8 = \boxed{}$

Find the unknown addend (unknown partner).

5. $3 + \boxed{} = 12$ $8 + \boxed{} = 13$ $15 - 7 = \boxed{}$

6. $6 + \boxed{} = 12$ $4 + \boxed{} = 13$ $18 - 9 = \boxed{}$

7. $7 + \boxed{} = 14$ $9 + \boxed{} = 17$ $16 - 9 = \boxed{}$

8. **Stretch Your Thinking** Draw hundred boxes, ten sticks, and circles to show a number between 100 and 200. What number did you show?

_____

Draw Quick Tens and Quick Hundreds

Homework

Draw the number using hundred boxes, ten sticks,
and circles. Then write the expanded form.

1.	**2.**	**3.**
176	143	184
100 + 70 + 6	___ + ___ + ___	___ + ___ + ___

What number is shown?   H = Hundreds, T = Tens, O = Ones

4.

___ H ___ T ___ O
  1   2   7

127 = 100 + 20 + 7

5.

___ H ___ T ___ O

___ = ___ + ___ + ___

6.

___ H ___ T ___ O

___ = ___ + ___ + ___

7.

___ H ___ T ___ O

___ = ___ + ___ + ___

Remembering

Write the unknown addend (partner).

1. $5 + \boxed{} = 15$ $17 - 9 = \boxed{}$ $7 + \boxed{} = 11$

2. $6 + \boxed{} = 14$ $16 - 7 = \boxed{}$ $3 + \boxed{} = 11$

3. $7 + \boxed{} = 15$ $12 - 7 = \boxed{}$ $6 + \boxed{} = 15$

Complete the addition doubles equation.

4. $\boxed{} + \boxed{} = 16$

5. $\boxed{} + \boxed{} = 10$

6. $\boxed{} + \boxed{} = 8$

7. $\boxed{} + \boxed{} = 14$

8. $\boxed{} + \boxed{} = 12$

9. $\boxed{} + \boxed{} = 18$

10. **Stretch Your Thinking** Show 194 two different ways.

_____

_____

Represent Numbers in Different Ways

Homework

Solve. Make a proof drawing.   **Show your work.**

I. Mina picks 63 flowers from her garden. She can
put 10 flowers in each vase. How many vases can
she fill? How many extra flowers will she have?

☐ vases   ☐ extra flowers

---

2. Luisa has 85 coupons. She can trade in 10 of
them for a toy. How many toys can Luisa get for
her coupons? How many coupons will she have
left over?

☐ toys   ☐ coupons left over

---

3. Dr. Turk wants to buy books that cost 10 dollars
each. He has 145 dollars. How many books
can he buy? How many dollars will he have
left over?

☐ books   ☐ dollars left over

---

4. The track team has 72 water bottles. They pack
them 10 to a box. How many boxes do they fill?
How many water bottles are left over?

☐ boxes   ☐ water bottles left over

Remembering

Make a drawing. Write an equation.
Solve the problem.   **Show your work.**

---

1. Amir had 9 books. He went to the library and got
   4 more. How many does he have now?

   ☐ _____
        label

---

2. Bella had 15 balloons. Some of the balloons flew
   away. Now she has 8 balloons left. How many
   balloons flew away?

   ☐ _____
        label

---

3. What number is 10 more than 9? Explain or
   show how you know.

   _____

4. Write the numbers from 34 to 44.

   _____

5. Stretch Your Thinking Make a math drawing
   to solve the word problem. There are 47 children
   in Ali's gym class. They need to stand in groups
   of 10. How many groups of children will there be?
   How many children will not be in a group of 10?

   ☐ groups   ☐ children not in a group of 10

Combine Ones, Tens, and Hundreds

Homework

Make a drawing for each number. Write <, >, or =.

1. 131 ◯ 141

2. 29 ◯ 28

3. 56 ◯ 56

4. 132 ◯ 38

Write <, >, or =.

5. 157 ◯ 175

6. 103 ◯ 107

7. 80 ◯ 18

8. 100 ◯ 100

9. 148 ◯ 149

10. 116 ◯ 99

11. 122 ◯ 150

12. 73 ◯ 111

13. 64 ◯ 64

14. 188 ◯ 186

Remembering

Add.

1. 40 + 30 = _____   60 + 20 = _____   90 + 10 = _____

   4 + 3 = _____   6 + 2 = _____   9 + 1 = _____

2. 50 + 50 = _____   70 + 20 = _____   80 + 20 = _____

   5 + 5 = _____   7 + 2 = _____   8 + 2 = _____

3. 20 + 50 = _____   30 + 20 = _____   40 + 50 = _____

   2 + 5 = _____   3 + 2 = _____   4 + 5 = _____

Draw the number using hundred boxes, ten sticks,
and circles. Then write the expanded form.

4.	5.
153	118
_____ + _____ + _____	_____ + _____ + _____

6. **Stretch Your Thinking** Which number is greater,
   134 or 143? Explain. Draw a picture if you like.

   _____

   _____

Compare Numbers Within 200

Homework

Add ones, tens, or a hundred.

1. $9 + 8 =$ _____ $7 + 7 =$ _____ $9 + 5 =$ _____

   $90 + 80 =$ _____ $70 + 70 =$ _____ $90 + 50 =$ _____

2. $6 + 8 =$ _____ $8 + 3 =$ _____ $9 + 7 =$ _____

   $60 + 80 =$ _____ $80 + 30 =$ _____ $90 + 70 =$ _____

3. $7 + 5 =$ _____ $6 + 9 =$ _____ $8 + 8 =$ _____

   $70 + 50 =$ _____ $60 + 90 =$ _____ $80 + 80 =$ _____

4. $8 + 7 =$ _____ $6 + 5 =$ _____ $9 + 4 =$ _____

   $80 + 70 =$ _____ $60 + 50 =$ _____ $90 + 40 =$ _____

5. $100 + 48 =$ _____ $21 + 100 =$ _____ $100 + 2 =$ _____

   $10 + 48 =$ _____ $21 + 10 =$ _____ $10 + 2 =$ _____

   $1 + 48 =$ _____ $21 + 1 =$ _____ $1 + 2 =$ _____

Remembering

1. Start with 10. Count by tens to 100.

_____

2. Write the numbers from 56 to 66.

_____

3. Write the numbers from 81 to 91.

_____

Draw the number using hundred boxes, ten sticks, and circles. Then write the expanded form.

4.	**5.**	**6.**
127	109	133
_100_ + _20_ + _7_	___ + ___ + ___	___ + ___ + ___

7. Stretch Your Thinking Add ones or tens.

$$4 + 4 = \underline{\hspace{1cm}} \qquad\qquad 3 + 6 = \underline{\hspace{1cm}}$$

$$40 + 40 = \underline{\hspace{1cm}} \qquad\qquad 30 + 60 = \underline{\hspace{1cm}}$$

$$140 + 40 = \underline{\hspace{1cm}} \qquad\qquad 130 + 60 = \underline{\hspace{1cm}}$$

Homework

Solve. Make a proof drawing.   **Show your work.**

1. Kivy makes 34 baskets. Her father makes 58 baskets. How many baskets do they make in all?

   [ ] _____
            label

2. Glen printed 67 posters yesterday and 86 more today. How many posters did he print altogether?

   [ ] _____
            label

Add.

3.   39   67   47
   + 44   + 56   + 98
   ____   ____   ____

4.   48   85   94
   + 33   + 68   + 57
   ____   ____   ____

Remembering

Make a drawing. Write an equation.
Solve the problem.   **Show your work.**

---

1. Elena set the table for 9 people. Three more people
came for dinner. How many people were there in all?

☐   _____
        label

---

2. Hector had 12 pennies. He lost 4 of them. How many
does he have now?

☐   _____
        label

---

3. Oni ate 3 cookies that she baked. She now has 9 left.
How many did she bake?

☐   _____
        label

---

4. Aisha found 9 shells at the beach. She now has 17 shells.
How many did she have before she went to the beach?

☐   _____
        label

---

5. Stretch Your Thinking Tisa collects animal stickers.
She had 96 stickers. She found 4 more stickers. Then
her cousin gave her 16 more. How many stickers does
she have now? Explain how you found your answer.

_____

_____

       Addition – Show All Totals Method

86	or	86	
+ 57		+ 57	
130		+	
		143	
+ 13			
143			

$$130 + 13 = 143$$

Add. Use any method.

1. 97   54   35
\+ 45   \+ 39   \+ 47

2. 56   76   86
\+ 77   \+ 88   \+ 65

3. 47   87   57
\+ 73   \+ 49   \+ 48

Remembering

Draw the number using hundred boxes, ten sticks,
and circles. Then write the expanded form.

1.	2.
185	132
____ + ____ + ____	____ + ____ + ____

Make a drawing for each number. Write <, >, or =.

3. 143 $\bigcirc$ 151

4. 87 $\bigcirc$ 87

Add ones or tens.

5. $9 + 9 =$ ____ $8 + 4 =$ ____ $8 + 6 =$ ____

  $90 + 90 =$ ____ $80 + 40 =$ ____ $80 + 60 =$ ____

6. Solve the word problem. Ida had a box
of 39 crayons. Juan gave her another
28 crayons. How many crayons does
she have now?

Show your work.

[ ] _____
         label

7. **Stretch Your Thinking** Add. Explain your method.

$$\begin{array}{r} 74 \\ + 67 \\ \hline \end{array}$$

_____

Addition – New Groups Below Method

Homework

$$
\begin{array}{r}
75 \\
+\,49 \\
\hline
110 \\
+\,14 \\
\hline
124
\end{array}
\qquad
\begin{array}{r}
75 \\
+\,49 \\
\hline
124
\end{array}
$$

or

$$110 + 14 = 124$$

Add. Use any method.

1.
$$
\begin{array}{r}
83 \\
+\,79 \\
\hline
\end{array}
\qquad
\begin{array}{r}
65 \\
+\,47 \\
\hline
\end{array}
\qquad
\begin{array}{r}
78 \\
+\,34 \\
\hline
\end{array}
$$

2.
$$
\begin{array}{r}
74 \\
+\,99 \\
\hline
\end{array}
\qquad
\begin{array}{r}
48 \\
+\,87 \\
\hline
\end{array}
\qquad
\begin{array}{r}
92 \\
+\,59 \\
\hline
\end{array}
$$

3.
$$
\begin{array}{r}
63 \\
+\,77 \\
\hline
\end{array}
\qquad
\begin{array}{r}
75 \\
+\,48 \\
\hline
\end{array}
\qquad
\begin{array}{r}
86 \\
+\,32 \\
\hline
\end{array}
$$

Remembering

Add.

1. $7 + 9 =$ ____ $5 + 8 =$ ____ $4 + 6 =$ ____

   $70 + 90 =$ ____ $50 + 80 =$ ____ $40 + 60 =$ ____

2. $100 + 36 =$ ____ $41 + 100 =$ ____ $100 + 67 =$ ____

   $10 + 36 =$ ____ $41 + 10 =$ ____ $10 + 67 =$ ____

   $1 + 36 =$ ____ $41 + 1 =$ ____ $1 + 67 =$ ____

Solve. Make a proof drawing.   **Show your work.**

3. Mrs. Martin makes 36 sandwiches for a school fair.
   Her friend makes 24 sandwiches. How many
   sandwiches do they make in all?

   ☐ _____
          label

4. Luis has a collection of 58 rocks. He finds
   44 more. How many rocks does he have now?

   ☐ _____
          label

Add. Use any method.

5.   74   58   45
   $+ 96$ $+ 69$ $+ 87$
   -----   -----   -----

6. **Stretch Your Thinking** Find the unknown addend.   57

$$\begin{array}{r} 57 \\ + \boxed{} \\ \hline 125 \end{array}$$

Practice Addition with Sums Over 100

Homework

Be the helper. Is the answer OK? Write *Yes* or *No*.
If *No*, fix the mistakes and write the correct answer.

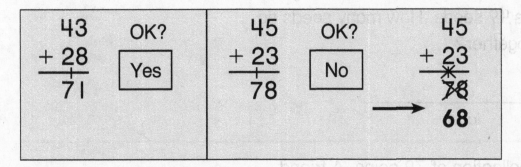

$$\begin{array}{r} 43 \\ + 28 \\ \hline 71 \end{array}$$ OK? Yes

$$\begin{array}{r} 45 \\ + 23 \\ \hline 78 \end{array}$$ OK? No

$$\begin{array}{r} 45 \\ + 23 \\ \hline \cancel{78} \end{array}$$ → **68**

1. $$\begin{array}{r} 27 \\ + 45 \\ \hline 72 \end{array}$$ OK? ☐

2. $$\begin{array}{r} 68 \\ + 26 \\ \hline 84 \end{array}$$ OK? ☐

3. $$\begin{array}{r} 32 \\ + 29 \\ \hline 511 \end{array}$$ OK? ☐

4. $$\begin{array}{r} 16 \\ + 67 \\ \hline 91 \end{array}$$ OK? ☐

5. $$\begin{array}{r} 59 \\ + 25 \\ \hline 74 \end{array}$$ OK? ☐

6. $$\begin{array}{r} 51 \\ + 44 \\ \hline 95 \end{array}$$ OK? ☐

7. $$\begin{array}{r} 85 \\ + 56 \\ \hline 141 \end{array}$$ OK? ☐

8. $$\begin{array}{r} 58 \\ + 99 \\ \hline 147 \end{array}$$ OK? ☐

9. $$\begin{array}{r} 73 \\ + 82 \\ \hline 165 \end{array}$$ OK? ☐

Remembering

Solve. Make a proof drawing.   **Show your work.**

1. Sara has 58 flower seeds to plant in her garden.
   Her father has 49 seeds. How many seeds do
   they have altogether?

   [ ] _____
                label

2. Oliver has a collection of 79 coins. A friend
   gives him 25 more coins. How many coins
   does he have in all?

   [ ] _____
                label

Add. Use any method.

3. $\begin{array}{r} 88 \\ + 56 \\ \hline \end{array}$ $\begin{array}{r} 75 \\ + 49 \\ \hline \end{array}$ $\begin{array}{r} 64 \\ + 28 \\ \hline \end{array}$

4. $\begin{array}{r} 99 \\ + 88 \\ \hline \end{array}$ $\begin{array}{r} 77 \\ + 44 \\ \hline \end{array}$ $\begin{array}{r} 69 \\ + 83 \\ \hline \end{array}$

5. **Stretch Your Thinking** Write a 2-digit addition exercise
   and find the sum.

   Example: $\begin{array}{r} 47 \\ + 56 \\ \hline 103 \end{array}$

Choose an Addition Method

Homework

Here are some more fruits and vegetables from the Farm Stand. Answer the questions below. Then draw the money amount. The first one is done for you.

Apples 79¢	Eggplant 96¢	Pears 58¢	Green Onions 67¢	Oranges 85¢

How much would you spend if you wanted to buy

1. apples and oranges?

_____164_____ ¢

$ _____1.64_____

2. apples and green onions?

_____ ¢

$ _____

3. pears and green onions?

_____ ¢

$ _____

4. eggplant and oranges?

_____ ¢

$ _____

Remembering

Add. Use any method.

1. 76
   + 38

   52
   + 39

   67
   + 88

2. 28
   + 96

   74
   + 39

   51
   + 89

Be the helper. Is the answer OK? Write *yes* or *no*.
If *no*, fix the mistakes and write the correct answer.

3. 28
   + 66
   ────
    94   OK? ▭

4. 61
   + 38
   ────
   109   OK? ▭

5. 57
   + 89
   ────
   147   OK? ▭

6. 33
   + 67
   ────
    90   OK? ▭

7. 82
   + 79
   ────
   161   OK? ▭

8. 54
   + 95
   ────
   159   OK? ▭

9. **Stretch Your Thinking** Doris buys some apples for
   69¢ and some pears for 78¢. She gives the cashier $1.50.
   Does she give the cashier enough money? Explain.

_____

Homework

Under the coins, write the total amount of money so far.
Then write the total using $. The first one is done for you.

1. 5¢   5¢   5¢   5¢

5¢   10¢   15¢   20¢ $ _0_ . _2_ _0_
                                                       total

2. 5¢   5¢   1¢   1¢   1¢

   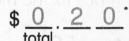

_____ $ ____ . ____ ____
                                                      total

3. 10¢   10¢   1¢   1¢   1¢   1¢

_____ $ ____ . ____ ____
                                                      total

4. 10¢   10¢   10¢   5¢   5¢   5¢

_____ $ ____ . ____ ____
                                                      total

5. Troy has 1 dime, 5 nickels, and 4 pennies.
Draw (10)s, (5)s, and (1)s.

Write the total amount of money. $ ____ . ____ ____
                                                                             total

Name _____

Remembering

Add. Use any method.

1.
$$68 + 57$$

$$85 + 29$$

$$94 + 76$$

Be the helper. Is the answer OK? Write *yes* or *no*.
If *no*, fix the mistakes and write the correct answer.

2.
$$\begin{array}{r} 52 \\ + 74 \\ \hline 126 \end{array}$$
OK? ☐

3.
$$\begin{array}{r} 84 \\ + 46 \\ \hline 140 \end{array}$$
OK? ☐

4.
$$\begin{array}{r} 63 \\ + 69 \\ \hline 122 \end{array}$$
OK? ☐

Answer the questions below. Then draw the money amount.

5. Dino bought a bunch of carrots for 89¢ and some celery for 78¢. How much did he spend?

_____

6. Tina bought a bunch of carrots for 88¢ and some celery for 58¢. How much did she spend?

_____

7. **Stretch Your Thinking** Draw 10 coins to show an amount between 50¢ and $1.00. Use only ⟨10⟩, ⟨5⟩, and ⟨1⟩. Make sure it is the fewest number of coins for that amount.

Pennies, Nickels, and Dimes

Name _____

Add.

1. 42
   + 54
   ____

2. 19
   + 64
   ____

3. 58
   + 32
   ____

4. 70
   + 23
   ____

5. 29
   + 29
   ____

6. 47
   + 34
   ____

7. 38
   + 62
   ____

8. 51
   + 20
   ____

9. 82
   + 17
   ____

10. Explain how you found the sum for Exercise 7.

_____

_____

_____

Remembering

Solve. Make a proof drawing. **Show your work.**

1. Sal goes to a plant nursery and sees 57 apple trees
   and 79 pear trees. How many trees does he see in all?

   ☐ _____
             label

2. Carol has a bag of red and yellow marbles. 48 of
   them are red and 63 of them are yellow. How
   many marbles does she have in total?

   ☐ _____
             label

Add. Use any method.

3.   47
    + 77

            91
           + 29

                38
               + 67

Be the helper. Is the answer OK? Write *yes* or *no*.
If *no*, fix the mistakes and write the correct answer.

4.   57
    + 49
    ———
    106   OK? ☐

5.   72
    + 39
    ———
    101   OK? ☐

6.   63
    + 78
    ———
    142   OK? ☐

7. **Stretch Your Thinking** Write an addition word
   problem using two 2-digit numbers. Solve the
   problem. Show your work.

   _____

   _____

Fluency: Addition within 100

Homework

Add.

1. $19 + 26 + 31 =$ _____

2. $25 + 36 + 27 =$ _____

3. $28 + 35 + 23 + 38 =$ _____

4. $17 + 44 + 56 + 30 =$ _____

Add Three or Four 2-Digit Addends **69**

Remembering

Add. Use any method.

1.
$$\begin{array}{r} 90 \\ + 80 \\ \hline \end{array}$$
$$\begin{array}{r} 69 \\ + 59 \\ \hline \end{array}$$
$$\begin{array}{r} 65 \\ + 38 \\ \hline \end{array}$$

2.
$$\begin{array}{r} 35 \\ + 89 \\ \hline \end{array}$$
$$\begin{array}{r} 53 \\ + 66 \\ \hline \end{array}$$
$$\begin{array}{r} 77 \\ + 91 \\ \hline \end{array}$$

Be the helper. Is the answer OK? Write *yes* or *no*.
If *no*, fix the mistakes and write the correct answer.

3.
$$\begin{array}{r} 58 \\ + 86 \\ \hline 144 \end{array}$$
OK? ☐

4.
$$\begin{array}{r} 71 \\ + 68 \\ \hline 149 \end{array}$$
OK? ☐

5.
$$\begin{array}{r} 87 \\ + 99 \\ \hline 185 \end{array}$$
OK? ☐

6. Add. Explain how you found the sum.

$$\begin{array}{r} 64 \\ + 36 \\ \hline \end{array}$$ _____

_____

_____

7. **Stretch Your Thinking** Write an addition exercise
using three 2-digit numbers. Find the sum.

© Houghton Mifflin Harcourt Publishing Company

Add Three or Four 2-Digit Addends

Homework

Solve each word problem.   **Show your work.**

1. Violet returns 4 bottles to the Recycle
   Center. She gets one nickel for each bottle.
   How much money does she get?

   _____

2. Jesse gets 40¢ for cans he brings to the
   Recycle Center. He gets 5¢ for each can.
   How many cans does he bring?

   ☐ _____
           label

3. Rosa brings 25 cans to the Recycling
   Center. Jorge brings 39 cans. How
   many cans do they bring altogether?

   ☐ _____
           label

4. Write a word problem of your own that is about
   recycling and has the answer *85 bottles*.

   _____

   _____

   _____

© Houghton Mifflin Harcourt Publishing Company

Remembering

Under the coins, write the total amount of money so far.
Then write the total using $.

1.

___ . ___ ___ ___ ___ $ ___ . ___ ___

2.

___ ___ ___ ___ ___ $ ___ . ___ ___

Add.

3. 45 + 19	**4.** 76 + 20	**5.** 67 + 23

Add.

6. $22 + 17 + 35 =$ ☐

7. $15 + 39 + 31 + 49 =$ ☐

8. Stretch Your Thinking Darif wants to buy 3 tickets

for a ride at the fair. Each ticket costs 39¢. Darif has $1.28.

How many tickets can he buy? _____

How much money will he spend? _____

Focus on Mathematical Practices

Homework

Use your centimeter ruler. Measure each horizontal line segment below by marking and counting 1-cm lengths.

1. ——————————————— ☐ cm

2. —————————————————— ☐ cm

3. —————————————— ☐ cm

4. Draw a line segment 8 cm long. Mark and count 1-cm lengths to check the length.

Measure each vertical line segment below by marking and counting 1-cm lengths.

5. | ☐ cm

6. | ☐ cm

7. | ☐ cm

Remembering

Make a ten to find the total.

1. $4 + 7 =$ ☐ $4 + 8 =$ ☐ $9 + 5 =$ ☐

2. $8 + 5 =$ ☐ $7 + 9 =$ ☐ $6 + 7 =$ ☐

Draw lines to make pairs.
Write odd or even.

3.

_____

4.

_____

Add.

5. $30 + 60 =$ _____ $50 + 20 =$ _____ $10 + 90 =$ _____

$3 + 6 =$ _____ $5 + 2 =$ _____ $1 + 9 =$ _____

6. **Stretch Your Thinking** Ryan measures the length of
his pen. He places the end of the pen at the 1-inch mark
of a ruler. Tell why the measurement will be wrong.

_____

_____

_____

Measure Length

Homework

Look for shapes in your home and neighborhood.

1. List or draw objects that show squares.

2. List or draw objects that show rectangles.

3. List or draw objects that show triangles.

4. List or draw objects that show pentagons.

5. List or draw objects that show hexagons.

Remembering

Find the unknown addend (unknown partner).

1. $4 + \boxed{} = 12$ $8 + \boxed{} = 15$ $14 - \boxed{} = 9$

2. $6 + \boxed{} = 12$ $5 + \boxed{} = 11$ $13 - \boxed{} = 7$

Find the total or partner.

3.
$$\begin{array}{cccccc} 7 & \quad 6 & \quad 9 & \quad 16 & \quad 12 & \quad 17 \\ +4 & \quad +8 & \quad +4 & \quad -\ 8 & \quad -\ 3 & \quad -\ 9 \end{array}$$

What numbers are shown?   H = Hundreds, T = Tens, O = Ones

4.

_____ H _____ T _____ O

_____ = _____ + _____ + _____

5.

_____ H _____ T _____ O

_____ = _____ + _____ + _____

6. **Stretch Your Thinking** Ian has 2 long straws and 2 short straws. How can he use all of the straws to make a triangle?

_____

_____

_____

Recognize and Draw Shapes

Homework

Use a centimeter ruler. Find the distance around each shape.

1.

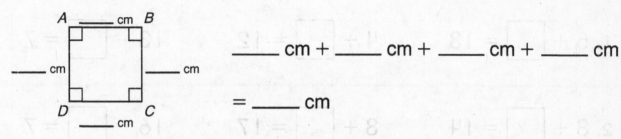

_____ cm + _____ cm + _____ cm + _____ cm

= _____ cm

2.

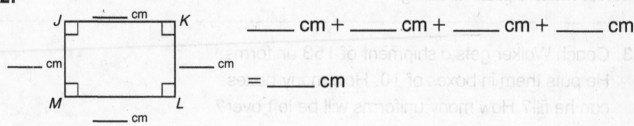

_____ cm + _____ cm + _____ cm + _____ cm

= _____ cm

Estimate and then measure each side.
Then find the distance around the rectangle.

3. a. Complete the table. Use a
centimeter ruler to measure.

Side	Estimate	Measure
HI		
IJ		
JK		
KH		

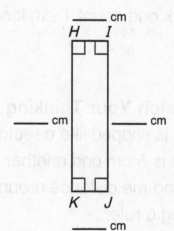

b. Find the distance around the rectangle.

_____ cm + _____ cm + _____ cm + _____ cm = _____ cm

Remembering

Write the unknown addend (unknown partner).

1. $5 + \boxed{} = 13$ $4 + \boxed{} = 12$ $13 - \boxed{} = 7$

2. $8 + \boxed{} = 14$ $8 + \boxed{} = 17$ $16 - \boxed{} = 7$

Solve. Make a proof drawing.   **Show your work.**

3. Coach Walker gets a shipment of 153 uniforms.
   He puts them in boxes of 10. How many boxes
   can he fill? How many uniforms will be left over?

   $\boxed{}$ boxes $\boxed{}$ uniforms left over

4. Draw a line segment 7 cm long.
   Mark and count 1-cm lengths to check the length.

5. **Stretch Your Thinking** Alex has a small notebook
   that is shaped like a rectangle. She knows one
   side is 6 cm and another side is 4 cm. Explain how
   to find the distance around the notebook without
   using a ruler.

   _____

   _____

   _____

Homework

Estimate and measure each side. Then find
the distance around the triangle.

1. a. Complete the table.

Side	Estimate	Measure
AB		
BC		
CA		

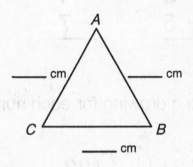

b. Find the distance around the triangle.

_____ cm + _____ cm + _____ cm = _____ cm

2. a. Complete the table.

Side	Estimate	Measure
DE		
EF		
FD		

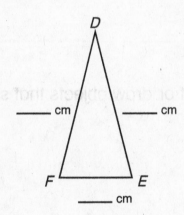

b. Find the distance around the triangle.

_____ cm + _____ cm + _____ cm = _____ cm

3. a. Complete the table.

Side	Estimate	Measure
JK		
KL		
LJ		

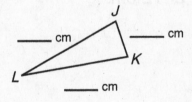

b. Find the distance around the triangle.

_____ cm + _____ cm + _____ cm = _____ cm

Remembering

Find the total or partner.

1.
$$\begin{array}{r} 8 \\ + 5 \\ \hline \end{array}$$
$$\begin{array}{r} 4 \\ + 7 \\ \hline \end{array}$$
$$\begin{array}{r} 6 \\ + 6 \\ \hline \end{array}$$
$$\begin{array}{r} 14 \\ - 5 \\ \hline \end{array}$$
$$\begin{array}{r} 13 \\ - 7 \\ \hline \end{array}$$
$$\begin{array}{r} 16 \\ - 9 \\ \hline \end{array}$$

Make a drawing for each number. Write $<$, $>$, or $=$.

2. 131 $\bigcirc$ 122

3. 27 $\bigcirc$ 35

4. List or draw objects that show rectangles.

5. **Stretch Your Thinking** Draw and label two different triangles. Each shape should have a distance around it of 12 cm.

Draw, Estimate, and Measure

Homework

Name the shapes using the words in the box.

cube   quadrilateral   pentagon   hexagon

1.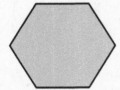

_____

2.

_____

3.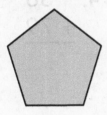

_____

4.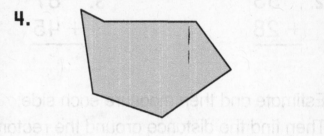

_____

5.

_____

6.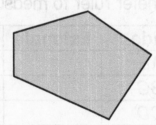

_____

7.

_____

8.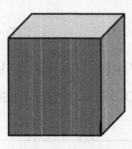

_____

Remembering

Make a drawing. Write an equation. Solve the problem.   **Show your work.**

1. Tanya bakes 12 muffins. She sells 9 of them at the bake sale. How many muffins does she have now?

   ☐ _____
   label

Add.

2. 53
   + 28

3. 87
   + 45

4. 36
   + 79

Estimate and then measure each side.
Then find the distance around the rectangle.

5. **a.** Complete the table. Use a centimeter ruler to measure.

Side	Estimate	Measure
AB		
BC		
CD		
DA		

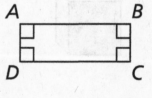

   b. Find the distance around the rectangle.

   _____ cm + _____ cm + _____ cm + _____ cm = _____ cm

6. **Stretch Your Thinking** Write all the names you can think of that could describe a four-sided shape.

   _____

   _____

Draw Using Faces

Homework

Complete the table. Estimate the height of six people, pets, or objects. Find the actual heights. Choose the nearest centimeter endpoint. Then, measure the difference between your estimate and the actual measurement.

Person, Pet, or Object	Estimated Height (cm)	Actual Height (cm)	Difference Between Estimated and Actual Height (cm)

Name _____

Remembering

Make a drawing. Write an equation. Solve the problem.   **Show your work.**

1. Chase has some music CDs. 9 of them are
   rock music. The other 8 are pop music. How
   many CDs does Chase have?

   ☐ _____
             label

Add. Use any method.

2.   68
   + 35
   _____

3.   52
   + 79
   _____

4.   84
   + 86
   _____

Estimate and then measure each side.
Then find the distance around the triangle.

5. **a.** Complete the table.

Side	Estimate	Measure
AB		
BC		
CA		

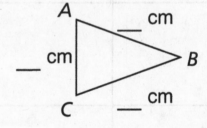

   b. Find the distance around the triangle.

   _____ cm + _____ cm + _____ cm = _____ cm

6. **Stretch Your Thinking** Find two items in the classroom
   whose lengths you estimate to have a difference of 3 cm.
   Then measure each item.

   Item 1 Estimate: _____ cm   Measure: _____ cm

   Item 2 Estimate: _____ cm   Measure: _____ cm

   Difference between Item 1 and Item 2: _____ cm

Estimate and Measure with Centimeters

Homework

1. Find five objects at home to measure in inches.
   Choose objects that are less than 1 yard (36 in.) long.
   Estimate and measure the length of each object.
   Measure to the nearest inch. Complete the table.

Object	Estimated Length (in.)	Measured Length (in.)

2. Plot the data from the last column in Exercise 1 on the line plot.

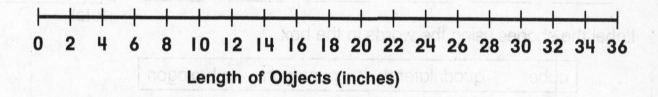

Length of Objects (inches)

3. Find five objects at home to measure in feet or yards.
   Complete the table. Remember to include units with
   your measurements.

Object	Estimated Length	Measured Length

Name

Remembering

Make a matching drawing or draw comparison
bars. Solve the problem.

Show your work.

1. Erin has 6 grapes. Cody has 8 more grapes
   than Erin. How many grapes does Cody have?

   _____
   label

Under the coins, write the total amount of money so far.
Then write the total using $.

2. 10¢   10¢   5¢   5¢   1¢   1¢

   _____   _____   _____   _____   _____   _____ $ ___ . ___
                                                                    total

Label the shapes using the words in the box.

| cube | quadrilateral | pentagon | hexagon |

3. 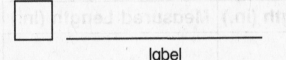   4.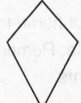

   _____   _____

5. **Stretch Your Thinking** Explain why we use rulers
   instead of hands or fingers to measure things.

   _____

   _____

Estimate and Measure with Inches

Name _____

1. Measure each line segment.

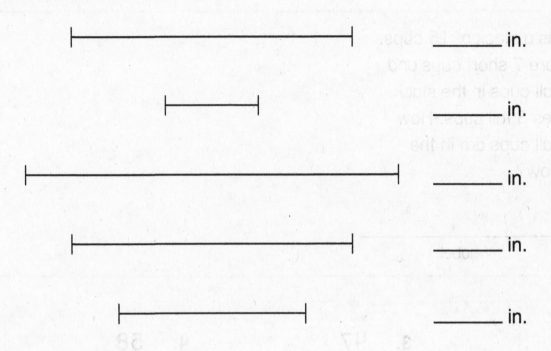

_____ in.

_____ in.

_____ in.

_____ in.

_____ in.

2. Show the data from Exercise 1 on this line plot.

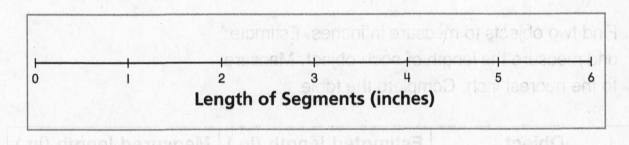

Length of Segments (inches)

3. Ring *more* or *less*.

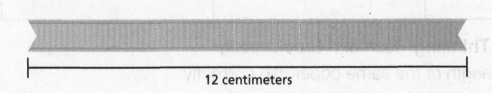

12 centimeters

The number of inches will be *more less* than the number
of centimeters.

Remembering

Solve the problem.   **Show your work.**

1. Mya has a stack of 15 cups.
   There are 7 short cups and
   some tall cups in the stack.
   She uses 3 tall cups. How
   many tall cups are in the
   stack now?

   ☐ _____
            label

Add.

2. 74
   + 15
   ‾‾‾‾

3. 47
   + 26
   ‾‾‾‾

4. 58
   + 34
   ‾‾‾‾

5. Find two objects to measure in inches. Estimate
   and measure the length of each object. Measure
   to the nearest inch. Complete the table.

Object	Estimated length (in.)	Measured length (in.)

6. **Stretch Your Thinking** Juan and Brooke each
   measured the length of the same paper clip correctly.
   Juan says the paper clip is about 5. Brooke says it is
   about 2. Explain how they can both be correct.

   _____

   _____

Homework

Color the quilt pattern. Use the table below.

Shape	Color
triangle	green
quadrilateral	red
pentagon	purple
hexagon	yellow

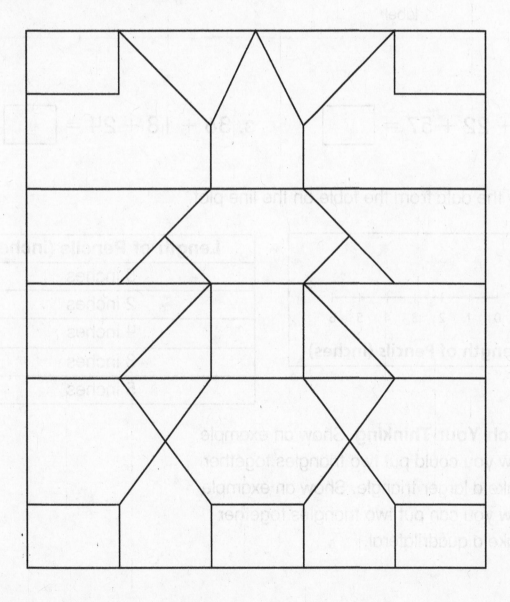

Remembering

Make a drawing. Write an equation.
Solve the problem.   **Show your work.**

1. Evan has 4 markers. That is 7 fewer markers
   than Jenna has. How many markers does
   Jenna have?

   ☐ _____
           label

Add.

2. $14 + 22 + 57 =$ ☐   3. $36 + 18 + 24 =$ ☐

4. Show the data from the table on the line plot.

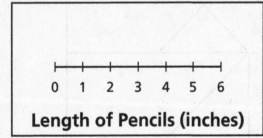

Length of Pencils (inches)

Length of Pencils (inches)
5 inches
2 inches
4 inches
3 inches
5 inches

5. **Stretch Your Thinking** Show an example
   of how you could put two triangles together
   to make a larger triangle. Show an example
   of how you can put two triangles together
   to make a quadrilateral.

Focus on Mathematical Practices

Homework

Draw coins to show 6 different ways to make
25¢ with pennies, nickels, and dimes.

1. 25¢	**2.** 25¢	**3.** 25¢
4. 25¢	**5.** 25¢	**6.** 25¢

Write how to count the money.

7.

  <u>25¢</u> <u>50¢</u> _____ _____ _____ _____

8.

  <u>25¢</u> <u>50¢</u> _____ _____ _____

Remembering

1. Write two equations for each Math Mountain.

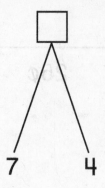

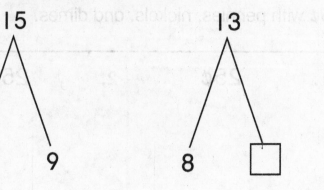

_____

_____

Add.

2. $40 + 60 =$ _____ $50 + 30 =$ _____ $10 + 40 =$ _____

$4 + 6 =$ _____ $5 + 3 =$ _____ $1 + 4 =$ _____

3. Draw a line segment 6 cm long.
Mark and count 1-cm lengths to check the length.

4. Stretch Your Thinking Elliot counts a group of coins
starting with the quarters. His sister counts the same
coins. She starts counting the pennies. Will they get
the same amount? Explain.

_____

_____

_____

Explore Quarters

Homework

Under each picture, write the total amount of money so far.
Then write the total using $.

1. 25¢   25¢   10¢   1¢

_____   _____   _____ $ _____ . _____ _____
                                                                     total

2.   100¢   5¢

_____   _____ $ _____ . _____ _____
                                                                    total

3. Hope has 1 dollar, 1 quarter, 5 dimes, 3 nickels,

and 2 pennies. Draw [100]s, (25)s, (10)s, (5)s, and (1)s.

Write the total amount of money. $ _____ . _____ _____
                                                                   total

Remembering

1. Complete the Math Mountains and equations.

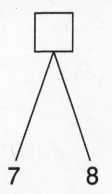

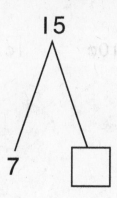

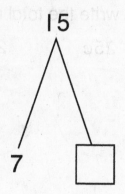

$7 + 8 = \boxed{}$ $7 + \boxed{} = 15$ $15 - 7 = \boxed{}$

Solve. Make a proof drawing.   **Show your work.**

2. Susan wins 78 tickets. She needs 10 tickets
for each prize. How many prizes can she get?
How many tickets will she have left over?

$\boxed{}$ prizes $\boxed{}$ tickets left over

---

3. Write how to count the money.

25¢ ____ ____ ____ ____ ____ ____ ____

4. Stretch Your Thinking Maria has $1.35. She
has only quarters and nickels. Draw two possible
groups of coins Maria could have. Use ⟨25⟩s to
show quarters and ⟨5⟩s to show nickels.

Homework

Name _____

Solve the word problems. Rewrite the 100 or make
a drawing. Add to check your answer.

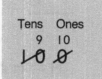 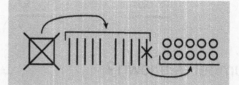

$$100 = \cancel{100} + \cancel{0}$$
$$\overset{90}{} \quad \overset{10}{}$$

1. There were 100 rubber ducks in the
   store. The shopkeeper sold 19 of them.
   How many ducks are in the store now?

   Show your work.

   ┌─────┐
   │   │ _____
   └─────┘
        label

2. Ben bought 100 napkins for the picnic.
   There are 26 napkins left after the picnic.
   How many napkins were used?

   ┌─────┐
   │   │ _____
   └─────┘
        label

Find the unknown addend. Check by adding.

3.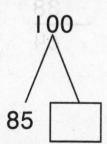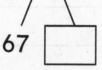

Remembering

Add or subtract.

1.   7   8   12   14   7   17

   +9   +5   −6   −6   +4   −9

What number is shown?   H = Hundreds, T = Tens, O = Ones

2. 

____ H ____ T ____ O

____ = ____ + ____ + ____

3.

____ H ____ T ____ O

____ = ____ + ____ + ____

Under each picture, write the total amount of
money so far. Then write the total using $.

4.   100¢   5¢   1¢

_____   _____   _____ $____ . ____ ____
                                                 total

5. Stretch Your Thinking Ed knows this answer
is wrong right away. How could he know this?

                                              100
                                           − 38

_____   64

_____

_____

                                               Addends and Subtraction

Homework

Solve each word problem. Make a
proof drawing if you need to.

Show your work.

---

1. Amon has 94 tomato seeds. He
uses 27 of them for a science
project. How many seeds does
he have left?

☐ _____
             label

---

2. Benita makes 56 leaf prints. She
gives 29 prints to her cousins. How
many prints does Benita have now?

☐ _____
             label

---

3. Denise has 71 straws. She uses
33 of them to make a bridge. How
many straws does she have left?

☐ _____
             label

---

4. Cedric has 70 sports cards. He gives
away 24 cards to his friends. How
many cards does Cedric have now?

☐ _____
             label

Remembering

Estimate and then measure each side.
Then find the distance around the rectangle.

1.

a. Complete the table. Use a
   centimeter ruler to measure.

Side	Estimate	Measure
AB		
BC		
CD		
DA		

b. Find the distance around the rectangle.

_____ cm + _____ cm + _____ cm + _____ cm = _____ cm

Solve the word problem. Rewrite the 100 or
make a drawing. Add to check your answer.   **Show your work.**

2. Amy has a box with 100 craft sticks in it. She
   uses some of them to make a project. There
   are 64 craft sticks left in the box. How many
   craft sticks did she use?

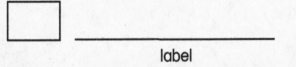

   label

---

3. Stretch Your Thinking Write a subtraction word
   problem with 29 as the answer.

_____

_____

_____

Subtraction Word Problems

Name _____

Homework

Expanded Method	**Ungroup First Method**	**Proof Drawing**
$$93 = \underset{\cancel{90}}{\overset{80}{}} + \underset{\cancel{3}}{\overset{+13}{}}$$ $$-57 = 50 + 7$$ $$\overline{\qquad 30 + 6 = 36}$$		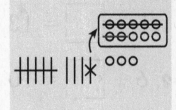

Subtract using any method.

1.
$$\begin{array}{r} 38 \\ -21 \\ \hline \end{array}$$

2.
$$\begin{array}{r} 57 \\ -39 \\ \hline \end{array}$$

3.
$$\begin{array}{r} 95 \\ -64 \\ \hline \end{array}$$

4.
$$\begin{array}{r} 50 \\ -13 \\ \hline \end{array}$$

5.
$$\begin{array}{r} 68 \\ -15 \\ \hline \end{array}$$

6.
$$\begin{array}{r} 77 \\ -29 \\ \hline \end{array}$$

7.
$$\begin{array}{r} 74 \\ -48 \\ \hline \end{array}$$

8.
$$\begin{array}{r} 84 \\ -49 \\ \hline \end{array}$$

Remembering

Write the unknown addend (partner).

1. $5 + \boxed{} = 13$ $15 - 9 = \boxed{}$ $4 + \boxed{} = 11$

2. $6 + \boxed{} = 10$ $13 - 6 = \boxed{}$ $12 - 7 = \boxed{}$

3. Under the coins, write the total amount of money so far.
Then write the total using $.

___ ___ ___ ___ ___ ___ $ ___.___ ___
                    total   total

Solve the word problem. Make a proof drawing
if you need to.

Show your work.

4. Jackson has 62 pennies in his jar. He
spends 38 of them. How many pennies
does he have now?

$\boxed{}$ _____
            label

5. Stretch Your Thinking How do you know if you need
to ungroup a ten for ones when subtracting?

_____

_____

_____

_____

Two Methods of Subtraction

Homework

Name

Subtract.

1. $\begin{array}{r} 87 \\ -59 \\ \hline \end{array}$

2. $\begin{array}{r} 63 \\ -14 \\ \hline \end{array}$

3. $\begin{array}{r} 55 \\ -18 \\ \hline \end{array}$

4. $\begin{array}{r} 73 \\ -17 \\ \hline \end{array}$

5. $\begin{array}{r} 83 \\ -12 \\ \hline \end{array}$

6. $\begin{array}{r} 99 \\ -35 \\ \hline \end{array}$

7. $\begin{array}{r} 62 \\ -55 \\ \hline \end{array}$

8. $\begin{array}{r} 71 \\ -49 \\ \hline \end{array}$

9. $\begin{array}{r} 45 \\ -26 \\ \hline \end{array}$

10. $\begin{array}{r} 50 \\ -11 \\ \hline \end{array}$

11. $\begin{array}{r} 92 \\ -44 \\ \hline \end{array}$

12. $\begin{array}{r} 75 \\ -52 \\ \hline \end{array}$

Remembering

Make a drawing. Write an equation.   **Show your work.**
Solve the problem.

1. Lily has 14 markers. Her
sister took some. Now Lily
has 8 markers. How many
did Lily's sister take?

☐ _____
           label

Add.

2.   57   73   89
   + 35   + 48   + 61

Subtract using any method.

3.   64   95   70
   − 27   − 37   − 41

4. Stretch Your Thinking Write and
solve a subtraction exercise where
you do not ungroup. Write and solve
a subtraction exercise where you
must ungroup.

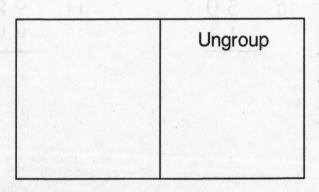

	Ungroup

Homework

Solve each word problem. Draw a
proof drawing if you need to.

Show your work.

---

1. There are 200 water bottles on a
table. The runners in a race take
73 of them. How many water bottles
are left on the table?

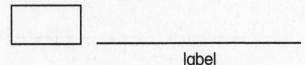

_____
label

---

2. There are 200 weeds in Kelly's
garden. Her little sister pulls out
44 of them. How many weeds are
still in the garden?

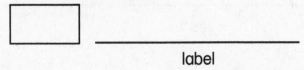

_____
label

Subtract.

```
3.  2 0 0        4.  2 0 0        5.  2 0 0
  –   6 6          –   8 2          –   5 4
```



```
6.  2 0 0        7.  2 0 0        8.  2 0 0
  –   9 5          –   3 8          –   4 7
```

Remembering

Make a drawing. Write an equation.   **Show your work.**
Solve the problem.

1. Sean finds 5 orange leaves and some
   yellow leaves. He finds 14 leaves in all.
   How many yellow leaves does he find?

   ┌──────┐ _____
   │   │
   └──────┘   label

Add. Use any method.

2.   48   64   74
   + 75   + 46   + 89
   ─────   ─────   ─────

Subtract.

3.   56   82   61
   − 19   − 53   − 46
   ─────   ─────   ─────

4. **Stretch Your Thinking** Suppose you subtract
   a 2-digit number from 200. Will you have to ungroup
   hundreds or tens? Explain. Give an example.

   _____

   _____

   _____

   _____

Name _____

Homework

Decide if you need to ungroup. Then subtract.

1. $\begin{array}{r} 147 \\ -\ 32 \\ \hline \end{array}$

2. $\begin{array}{r} 147 \\ -\ 38 \\ \hline \end{array}$

3. $\begin{array}{r} 147 \\ -\ 48 \\ \hline \end{array}$

4. $\begin{array}{r} 126 \\ -\ 54 \\ \hline \end{array}$

5. $\begin{array}{r} 126 \\ -\ 57 \\ \hline \end{array}$

6. $\begin{array}{r} 126 \\ -\ 97 \\ \hline \end{array}$

7. $\begin{array}{r} 187 \\ -\ 46 \\ \hline \end{array}$

8. $\begin{array}{r} 187 \\ -\ 49 \\ \hline \end{array}$

9. $\begin{array}{r} 187 \\ -\ 99 \\ \hline \end{array}$

10. $\begin{array}{r} 172 \\ -\ 35 \\ \hline \end{array}$

11. $\begin{array}{r} 172 \\ -\ 85 \\ \hline \end{array}$

12. $\begin{array}{r} 172 \\ -\ 31 \\ \hline \end{array}$

Remembering

Make a drawing. Write an equation. Solve the problem.

Show your work.

1. The coach gives out 8 large water bottles and 8 small water bottles. How many water bottles does the coach give out?

☐ _____
　　　label

Add. Use any method.

2.　　66　　　　　　97　　　　　　53
　　+ 77　　　　　+ 84　　　　　+ 79

Subtract.

3.　2 0 0　　　　　2 0 0　　　　　2 0 0
　　－ 4 1　　　　　－ 7 3　　　　　－ 5 7

4. **Stretch Your Thinking** Use the numbers below to complete the subtraction problem. Place the numbers so that you must ungroup two times. Then subtract.

　3　　　6　　　9　　　5

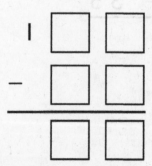

Homework

Decide if you need to ungroup. Then subtract.

1.   1 3 0
   − 9 9
   ‾‾‾‾‾‾

2.   1 5 0
   − 3 9
   ‾‾‾‾‾‾

3.   1 6 0
   − 6 7
   ‾‾‾‾‾‾

4.   1 0 8
   − 8 8
   ‾‾‾‾‾‾

5.   1 2 0
   − 8 3
   ‾‾‾‾‾‾

6.   1 0 1
   − 7 2
   ‾‾‾‾‾‾

Solve each word problem.   **Show your work.**

7. There were 120 nickels in a jar.
   Janice took out 49 nickels. How
   many nickels are in the jar now?

   ☐ _____
       label

8. Last week, there were 109 books
   at the bookstore. So far, 25 books
   have been sold. How many
   books have not been sold?

   ☐ _____
       label

Remembering

Add. Use doubles.

1. $6 + 7 =$ ☐ $8 + 7 =$ ☐ $6 + 5 =$ ☐

2. $9 + 7 =$ ☐ $11 + 9 =$ ☐ $8 + 6 =$ ☐

Estimate and then measure each side.
Then find the distance around the triangle.

3.

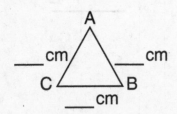

a. Complete the table.

Side	Estimate	Measure
AB		
BC		
CA		

b. Find the distance around the triangle.

_____ cm + _____ cm + _____ cm = _____ cm

Decide if you need to ungroup. Then subtract.

4.
```
  1 6 9
-   4 4
-------
```
```
  1 8 5
-   7 9
-------
```
```
  1 3 2
-   6 8
-------
```

5. **Stretch Your Thinking** Look at Evan's
subtraction problem. What did he do wrong?
Find the correct answer.

```
  1 0 7
-   6 8
-------
    4 9
```

_____

_____

    Zero in the Ones or Tens Place

Name _____

Homework

What would you like to buy? First, see how
much money you have. Pay for the item.
How much money do you have left?

Yard Sale

Globe
85¢

Ring
67¢

Sports Bag
98¢

Eraser
79¢

Color Pencils
66¢

---

1. I have 124¢ in my pocket.

I bought the _____.

```
  1 2 4¢
-       ¢
_____
```

I have _____ ¢ left.

2. I have 152¢ in my pocket.

I bought the _____.

```
  1 5 2¢
-       ¢
_____
```

I have _____ ¢ left.

---

3. I have 145¢ in my pocket.

I bought the _____.

```
  1 4 5¢
-       ¢
_____
```

I have _____ ¢ left.

4. I have 131¢ in my pocket.

I bought the _____.

```
  1 3 1¢
-       ¢
_____
```

I have _____ ¢ left.

Remembering

Find the total or partner.

1. $\begin{array}{r} 7 \\ +6 \\ \hline \end{array}$ $\begin{array}{r} 9 \\ +5 \\ \hline \end{array}$ $\begin{array}{r} 8 \\ +9 \\ \hline \end{array}$ $\begin{array}{r} 15 \\ -6 \\ \hline \end{array}$ $\begin{array}{r} 12 \\ -8 \\ \hline \end{array}$ $\begin{array}{r} 16 \\ -9 \\ \hline \end{array}$

Label the shapes using the words in the box.

| cube | quadrilateral | pentagon | hexagon |

2.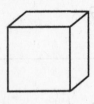

_____

3.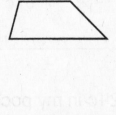

_____

Solve the word problem. **Show your work.**

4. Logan buys a notebook with
106 pages. He uses 29 of the
pages. How many pages are
not used?

[   ] _____
label

5. **Stretch Your Thinking** Kayla has 135¢. She buys
a toy and has 78¢ left. What is the price of the toy
she buys?

_____

Model Subtraction with Money

Subtract.

1. $\begin{array}{r} 29 \\ -13 \\ \hline \end{array}$

2. $\begin{array}{r} 54 \\ -26 \\ \hline \end{array}$

3. $\begin{array}{r} 75 \\ -25 \\ \hline \end{array}$

4. $\begin{array}{r} 48 \\ -38 \\ \hline \end{array}$

5. $\begin{array}{r} 90 \\ -57 \\ \hline \end{array}$

6. $\begin{array}{r} 17 \\ -8 \\ \hline \end{array}$

7. $\begin{array}{r} 100 \\ -42 \\ \hline \end{array}$

8. $\begin{array}{r} 63 \\ -22 \\ \hline \end{array}$

9. $\begin{array}{r} 97 \\ -59 \\ \hline \end{array}$

10. Explain how you found the difference for Exercise 7.

_____

_____

Remembering

Make a matching drawing or draw comparison
bars. Solve the problem.   **Show your work.**

1. Jayden has 8 grapes. Ashley has
6 more grapes than Jayden has.
How many grapes does Ashley
have?

┌─────┐ _____
│   │
└─────┘   label

Which sticker would you like to buy? First, see how
much money you have. Pay for the sticker. How
much money do you have left?

Sticker Sale

Smile	Heart	Sun	Moon
78¢	89¢	76¢	97¢

2. I have 132¢ in my pocket.

I bought the _____.

  132¢
−   ¢
_____

I have _____ ¢ left.

3. I have 164¢ in my pocket.

I bought the _____.

  164¢
−   ¢
_____

I have _____ ¢ left.

4. Stretch Your Thinking Subtract.
Which subtraction takes longer to do? Explain.

A   64
    − 31
    _____

B   92
    − 47
    _____

_____

Name _____

Homework

Draw a Math Mountain to solve each word problem. Show how you add or subtract.

Show your work.

---

1. Papi has 148 slices of pizza in his shop. He sells 56 slices. How many slices does Papi have left?

   ☐ _____

   label

---

2. There are 34 children at the park. Then 16 children join them. How many children are at the park now?

   ☐ _____

   label

---

3. Bella has 19 crayons. She gives 12 of them to her friend. How many crayons does she have left?

   ☐ _____

   label

---

4. Seventy-nine girls and forty-eight boys are in Grade 2 at Center School. How many children are in Grade 2?

   ☐ _____

   label

Remembering

Make a drawing. Write an equation.   **Show your work.**
Solve the problem.

1. Luke has 7 trucks. Zoe has 6 more
   trucks than Luke. How many trucks
   does Zoe have?

   ☐ _____
              label

---

2. Show the data from the table on the line plot.

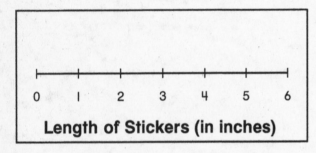

Length of Stickers (in inches)

Length of Stickers (in inches)
5 inches
3 inches
4 inches
2 inches
3 inches

Subtract.

3. 54
  − 31

4. 81
  − 26

5. 74
  − 7

6. **Stretch Your Thinking** Write and solve
   a subtraction word problem that starts with
   146. The answer should be less than 100.

   _____

   _____

Word Problems with Addition and Subtraction

Homework

Name _____

1. Write all of the equations for 74, 25, and 49.

74

25   49

$25 + 49 = 74$ _____

$74 = 25 + 49$ _____

_____   _____

_____   _____

_____   _____

2. Write all of the equations for 157, 68, and 89.

157

68   89

$68 + 89 = 157$ _____

$157 = 68 + 89$ _____

_____   _____

_____   _____

_____   _____

Remembering

Add in any order. Write the total.

1. $6 + 3 + 5 = \boxed{}$ $9 + 2 + 9 = \boxed{}$ $3 + 5 + 7 = \boxed{}$

2. $8 + 7 + 2 = \boxed{}$ $7 + 3 + 8 = \boxed{}$ $5 + 8 + 4 = \boxed{}$

Make a drawing for each number. Write $<$, $>$, or $=$.

3. $122 \bigcirc 131$

4. $35 \bigcirc 28$

Draw a Math Mountain to solve the word problem. Show how you add or subtract.

Show your work.

5. Berry Elementary School has 127 children. 69 of the children are girls. How many children are boys?

$\boxed{}$
_____
label

6. **Stretch Your Thinking** When would there be only four different equations for a set of Math Mountain numbers? Give an example.

_____

Equations with Greater Numbers

Homework

Add or subtract. Watch the sign!

1. $\begin{array}{r} 75 \\ +\ 25 \\ \hline \end{array}$

2. $\begin{array}{r} 14 \\ +\ 6 \\ \hline \end{array}$

3. $\begin{array}{r} 47 \\ +\ 38 \\ \hline \end{array}$

4. $\begin{array}{r} 87 \\ -\ 48 \\ \hline \end{array}$

5. $\begin{array}{r} 34 \\ +\ 18 \\ \hline \end{array}$

6. $\begin{array}{r} 27 \\ -\ 8 \\ \hline \end{array}$

7. $\begin{array}{r} 100 \\ -\ 85 \\ \hline \end{array}$

8. $\begin{array}{r} 67 \\ -\ 29 \\ \hline \end{array}$

9. $\begin{array}{r} 58 \\ +\ 37 \\ \hline \end{array}$

10. $\begin{array}{r} 81 \\ -\ 53 \\ \hline \end{array}$

11. $\begin{array}{r} 47 \\ +\ 37 \\ \hline \end{array}$

12. $\begin{array}{r} 99 \\ -\ 39 \\ \hline \end{array}$

Remembering

Make a drawing. Write an equation.   **Show your work.**
Solve the problem.

1. Mayumi shops with her mom.
   She puts 8 oranges in the basket.
   Her mom puts in 7 more oranges.
   How many oranges are in the
   basket now?

   ┌──────────┐
   │   │   _____
   └──────────┘
            label

2. Write all of the equations for 83, 35, 48.

$$83$$

$$35 \qquad 48$$

$35 + 48 = 83$ _____ $83 = 35 + 48$ _____

_____   _____

_____   _____

_____   _____

3. **Stretch Your Thinking** Allison solved this
   problem. Is she correct? If not, explain and solve.

$$\begin{array}{r} 46 \\ + 17 \\ \hline 53 \end{array}$$

_____

_____

Practice Addition and Subtraction

Homework

Mr. Green wants to buy some things at a
flea market. He will pay for the items with
one dollar (100 cents). How much change
will he get back?

Mittens	Toy Binoculars	Toy Camera	Toy Lamb	Plant
17¢	39¢	46¢	28¢	52¢

1. Mr. Green buys the mittens
and the plant.

_____ ¢

+ _____ ¢

Total: _____

100¢ − _____ = _____

His change will be _____ ¢.

2. Mr. Green buys the toy lamb
and the toy camera.

_____ ¢

+ _____ ¢

Total: _____

100¢ − _____ = _____

His change will be _____ ¢.

3. Mr. Green buys the toy
binoculars and the toy lamb.

_____ ¢

+ _____ ¢

Total: _____

100¢ − _____ = _____

His change will be _____ ¢.

4. Mr. Green buys the toy camera
and the plant.

_____ ¢

+ _____ ¢

Total: _____

100¢ − _____ = _____

His change will be _____ ¢.

Buy and Sell with One Dollar **119**

Remembering

Add or subtract.

1.
$$\begin{array}{r} 5 \\ +4 \\ \hline \end{array} \qquad \begin{array}{r} 9 \\ +6 \\ \hline \end{array} \qquad \begin{array}{r} 6 \\ +8 \\ \hline \end{array} \qquad \begin{array}{r} 13 \\ -8 \\ \hline \end{array} \qquad \begin{array}{r} 18 \\ -9 \\ \hline \end{array} \qquad \begin{array}{r} 14 \\ -9 \\ \hline \end{array}$$

Cross out the extra information or write hidden or missing information. Then solve the problem.

Show your work.

2. Latisha has some apples. She buys
5 more. How many apples does
she have now?

▢ _____

label

Add or subtract. Watch the sign!

3.
$$\begin{array}{r} 73 \\ -38 \\ \hline \end{array} \qquad \begin{array}{r} 56 \\ +27 \\ \hline \end{array} \qquad \begin{array}{r} 100 \\ -47 \\ \hline \end{array}$$

4. **Stretch Your Thinking** Rashid has one dollar
(100 cents). He wants to buy a ball for 50 cents.
He also wants to buy two other toys and still have
money left over. Explain what Rashid needs to
do when choosing the two toys.

_____

_____

_____

Name _____

Homework

Add up to solve each word problem. **Show your work.**

1. Rudy has 45 ants in his ant farm. He adds some
   more ants to the ant farm. Now there are 69 ants.
   How many ants does Rudy add to the ant farm?

   ☐ _____

           label

2. Tina has 92 flowers in her garden this morning.
   After she takes some flowers to school, there
   are 33 flowers in her garden. How many flowers
   does Tina take to school?

   ☐ _____

           label

3. Lia collects 86 buttons. Then she gives some
   to Matt. Now Lia has 61 buttons. How many
   buttons does Lia give to Matt?

   ☐ _____

           label

4. There were 73 cars in the garage this morning.
   Now there are 24 cars in the garage. How
   many cars left the garage?

   ☐ _____

           label

Word Problems with Unknown Addends **121**

Remembering

Add. Use doubles.

1. $5 + 6 = \boxed{}$ $9 + 7 = \boxed{}$ $10 + 8 = \boxed{}$

2. $7 + 8 = \boxed{}$ $8 + 8 = \boxed{}$ $7 + 6 = \boxed{}$

Mia and Tom buy things at the school store. They will
each pay for the items with one dollar (100 cents).
How much change will they each get back?

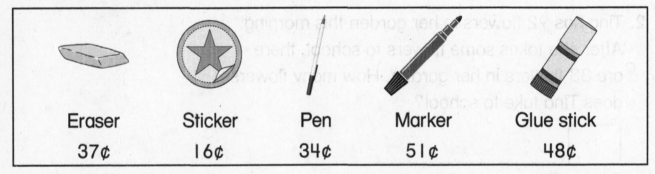

Eraser	Sticker	Pen	Marker	Glue stick
37¢	16¢	34¢	51¢	48¢

3. Mia buys the marker and the
   sticker.

   _____ ¢

   + _____ ¢

   Total: _____ ¢

   100¢ − _____ = _____

   Her change will be _____ ¢.

4. Tom buys the eraser and the
   glue stick.

   _____ ¢

   + _____ ¢

   Total: _____ ¢

   100¢ − _____ = _____

   His change will be _____ ¢.

---

5. **Stretch Your Thinking** Use the pictures and prices above.
   Suppose Mia has another 100 cents and buys one item. If she
   has 66¢ left, how can you tell which item she bought? Explain.

    Word Problems with Unknown Addends

Homework

Solve each word problem.   **Show your work.**

---

1. Alma and Larry have stickers to put on their
   poster. Alma has 28 stickers. They have
   84 stickers in all. How many stickers does
   Larry have?

   ☐ _____
                label

---

2. There are 61 magazines in the library. Then
   more magazines are delivered. Now there are
   100 magazines. How many new magazines
   are delivered to the library?

   ☐ _____
                label

---

3. Mori puts 95 pretzels in a bowl. Her friends
   eat some. Now there are 72 pretzels in the
   bowl. How many pretzels do her friends eat?

   ☐ _____
                label

---

4. Eric's basketball team scores 36 points in
   the first game. They score some points in the
   second game. In the two games, they score
   52 points in all. How many points do they
   score in the second game?

   ☐ _____
                label

Remembering

Use your centimeter ruler. Measure the horizontal line
segment below by marking and counting 1-cm lengths.

1.

_____ cm

Add ones or tens.

2. $5 + 6 =$ ☐ $8 + 7 =$ ☐ $9 + 4 =$ ☐

$50 + 60 =$ ☐ $80 + 70 =$ ☐ $90 + 40 =$ ☐

Add up to solve the word problem.   **Show your work.**

3. Austin has 65 United States stamps. He
gets more stamps from other countries.
Now he has 84 stamps. How many stamps
are from other countries?

☐ _____
label

4. Stretch Your Thinking Look at Problem 3. Did you
add to solve the problem? Explain.

_____

_____

_____

     More Word Problems with Unknown Addends

Homework

Write an equation. Solve the word problem.

1. Abigail's mother gives her some carrots to sell at the state fair. Abigail picks 16 more carrots from the garden. Now Abigail has 73 carrots to sell. How many carrots did her mother give her?

☐ _____
label

2. Stanley the grocer has lots of onions. He sells 44 onions in the morning. Now he has 48 onions left to sell. How many onions did Stanley have to begin with?

☐ _____
label

3. At the end of the first half of the basketball game, Carmen's team has 23 points. At the end of the second half, they have 52 points. How many points did Carmen's team score in the second half of the game?

☐ _____
label

4. Mr. Art has 88 sheets of paper in his cabinet. He gives some paper to his students. Then he has 61 sheets of paper left. How many sheets of paper did Mr. Art give to his students?

☐ _____
label

Name _____

Remembering

Find the unknown addend (unknown partner).

1. $5 + \boxed{} = 13$ $\qquad$ $16 - 7 = \boxed{}$ $\qquad$ $6 + \boxed{} = 14$

2. $9 + \boxed{} = 16$ $\qquad$ $15 - 8 = \boxed{}$ $\qquad$ $13 - 7 = \boxed{}$

3. **Draw a Picture and Explain** Draw two different Math Mountains with a total of 13. Explain why you can make two different Math Mountains.

_____

_____

_____

_____

Solve the word problem.

Show your work.

4. Erin has 56 crayons. She gets some new ones. Now she has 82 crayons. How many new crayons did she get?

$\boxed{}$ _____
label

5. **Stretch Your Thinking** Write and solve a word problem that has an unknown start number. Use 2-digit numbers.

_____

_____

$\qquad$ *Start Unknown* Problems

Name _____

Homework

Draw comparison bars and write an equation to solve each problem.

1. Tran has 29 seashells. Vimi has 63 seashells. How many fewer seashells does Tran have than Vimi?

[ ] _____
      label

2. Justine and Morgan are buying feathers at the craft store. Morgan buys 17 more feathers than Justine. Morgan buys 76 feathers. How many feathers does Justine buy?

[ ] _____
      label

3. Ali has 54 guppies in her fish tank. Peter has 28 more guppies than Ali. How many guppies does Peter have in his fish tank?

[ ] _____
      label

4. Stanley the grocer buys 91 bags of flour for his store. Ted buys 46 fewer bags of flour than Stanley. How many bags of flour does Ted buy?

[ ] _____
      label

Compare Word Problems **127**

Remembering

Draw lines to make pairs. Write odd or even.

1. ● ● ● ● ● ●
    ● ● ● ● ● ●

2.

_____

Be the helper. Is the answer OK? Write *yes* or *no*.
If *no*, fix the mistake and write the correct answer.

3. $\begin{array}{r} 59 \\ + 23 \\ \hline 82 \end{array}$ OK? ▢

4. $\begin{array}{r} 16 \\ + 58 \\ \hline 64 \end{array}$ OK? ▢

5. $\begin{array}{r} 37 \\ + 49 \\ \hline 716 \end{array}$ OK? ▢

Write an equation. Solve the word problem.

6. Mrs. Patel has some plates.
   She uses 37 of them at the
   picnic. She has 58 plates left.
   How many plates were in the
   stack to start with?

   _____
   label

7. **Stretch Your Thinking** Write and solve
   a word problem that matches the drawing.

   _____

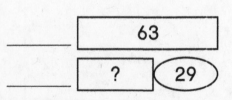

   _____

   _____

    Compare Word Problems

Make a drawing. Write an equation. Solve.

---

1. Mariko has 63 photos in her photo book.
   That is 23 fewer photos than Sharon has.
   How many photos does Sharon have?

   ☐ _____

            label

---

2. Fred has some crayons. He gives Drew
   26 crayons. Now Fred has 42 crayons.
   How many crayons did Fred start with?

   ☐ _____

            label

---

3. Marisa brings out 60 bowls for the party.
   Thirty-five of the bowls are large. The
   rest are small. How many small bowls
   does Marisa bring out?

   ☐ _____

            label

---

4. Sean sells 35 tickets for the school play.
   If he sells 24 more tickets, he will sell all
   the tickets he had at the start. How many
   tickets did Sean start with?

   ☐ _____

            label

Remembering

Add.

1. $15 + 29 + 34 =$ _____

2. $23 + 38 + 27 + 59 =$ _____

Solve the word problem.   **Show your work.**

3. Carter has 5 jersey shirts, 4 solid shirts, and some plaid shirts. He has 15 shirts altogether. How many plaid shirts does he have?

☐ _____
      label

Draw comparison bars and write an equation to solve the problem.

4. Max has 72 pennies. Jada has 34 fewer pennies than Max. How many pennies does Jada have?

☐ _____
      label

5. **Stretch Your Thinking** Write and solve a word problem that matches the drawing.

_____

_____

_____

Ryan	55	
Erin	?	29

Mixed Word Problems

Homework

Think about the first-step question.
Then solve the problem.

---

1. Luisa has 35 building blocks. Jack gives
her 18 more blocks. Luisa uses 26 blocks
to build a castle. How many blocks are
not used in the castle?

☐ _____
    label

---

2. There are 45 red apples and 24 green
apples for sale at a farm stand. The farmer
sells some apples. Now she has 36 apples
left. How many apples does the farmer sell?

☐ _____
    label

---

3. Maria has 16 more beads than Gus.
Gus has 24 beads. Denise has 12 more
beads than Maria. How many beads does
Denise have?

☐ _____
    label

Name

Remembering

Find the total or partner.

1.
$$7 \atop +8$$
$$6 \atop +8$$
$$9 \atop +6$$
$$16 \atop -8$$
$$12 \atop -7$$
$$17 \atop -9$$

2. Look for shapes in your classroom and school.
List or draw objects that show triangles.

Make a drawing. Write an equation. Solve.

3. Eric has 53 baseball cards.
17 cards are new. The rest are old.
How many baseball cards
are old?

_____
label

4. **Stretch Your Thinking** Write a 2-step
word problem that uses subtraction then
addition. Solve.

_____

_____

2-Step Word Problems

Homework

Think about the first-step question.
Then solve the problem.

---

1. There are 45 children at the park in the morning.
   25 are boys and the rest are girls. Some more
   girls come to the park in the afternoon. Now there
   are 30 girls at the park. How many girls come
   to the park in the afternoon?

   ☐ _____
        label

---

2. Jonah has 36 sheets of green paper and
   26 sheets of blue paper. He gives some
   sheets of green paper to Tova. Now he has
   42 sheets of paper. How many sheets of
   green paper does he give Tova?

   ☐ _____
        label

---

3. There are 16 mystery books, 22 history books,
   and 21 science books in a large bookcase.
   A smaller bookcase has 30 fewer books.
   How many books are in the smaller bookcase?

   ☐ _____
        label

Name _____

Remembering

Estimate and then measure each side.
Then find the distance around the rectangle.

1.

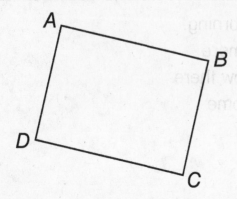

a. Complete the table. Use a centimeter ruler to measure.

Side	Estimate	Measure
AB		
BC		
CD		
DA		

b. Find the distance around the rectangle.

_____ cm + _____ cm + _____ cm + _____ cm = _____ cm

Think about the first-step question. Then solve the problem.

2. Kate has 37 old crayons and 45 new crayons. She gives some crayons to Sam. Now she has 56 crayons. How many crayons did she give to Sam?

[ ] _____
          label

---

3. **Stretch Your Thinking** Use the information in the table to write a 2-step word problem. Then solve.

Points Scored	
Will	47
Ava	29
Cody	35

_____

_____

More 2-Step Word Problems

Name

Homework

The children on the math team each measured the length of one of their feet. They made a table to show their data.

Length of Foot

Name	Length
Marta	19 cm
Pete	18 cm
Alberto	20 cm
Miko	13 cm
Sasha	16 cm

Use the table to solve each word problem.

Show your work.

1. How much longer is Alberto's foot than Pete's?

   ☐ _____

          label

2. Which child has a foot that is 3 cm longer than Sasha's?

   _____

3. Miko's foot is 2 cm shorter than Jon's. What is the length of Jon's foot?

   ☐ _____

          label

4. Use the information in the table to write your own problem. Solve the problem.

   _____

   _____

   _____

Remembering

Complete the addition doubles equation.

1. $\boxed{} + \boxed{} = 14$

2. $\boxed{} + \boxed{} = 8$

3. $\boxed{} + \boxed{} = 6$

4. $\boxed{} + \boxed{} = 18$

Add.

5.
$$\begin{array}{r} 46 \\ + 28 \\ \hline \end{array} \qquad \begin{array}{r} 34 \\ + 57 \\ \hline \end{array} \qquad \begin{array}{r} 69 \\ + 52 \\ \hline \end{array}$$

Think about the first-step question. Then solve the problem.

6. The coach gets a delivery of 24 large uniforms, 18 medium uniforms, and 25 small uniforms. He returns 19 of the uniforms. How many uniforms does the coach have now?

$\boxed{}$ _____
label

7. **Stretch Your Thinking** Use a centimeter ruler to measure four objects. Record each length. Then write a question and solve.

_____

_____

_____

Object	Length

© Houghton Mifflin Harcourt Publishing Company

Focus on Mathematical Practices

Homework

Write the time in two different ways.

1.

_____ o'clock

2.

_____ o'clock

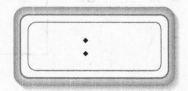

3.

_____ o'clock

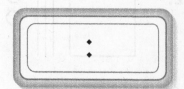

Draw the hands on each analog clock and write the time on each digital clock below.

4.

1 o'clock

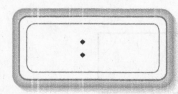

5.

6 o'clock

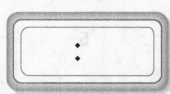

6.

12 o'clock

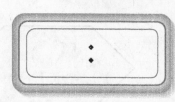

For each activity, ring the appropriate time.

7. eat an afternoon snack

3:00 A.M.   2:00 P.M.   6:00 P.M.

8. go to a movie after dinner

8:00 A.M.   12:00 NOON   7:00 P.M.

Remembering

Add.

1.
$$4 + 7$$
$$6 + 9$$
$$3 + 7$$
$$5 + 2$$
$$8 + 8$$
$$9 + 1$$

What number is shown?   H = Hundreds, T = Tens, O = Ones

2.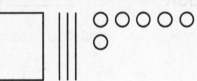

_____ H _____ T _____ O

_____ = _____ + _____ + _____

3.

_____ H _____ T _____ O

_____ = _____ + _____ + _____

Label the shapes using the words in the box.

cube   quadrilateral   pentagon   hexagon

4.

_____

5.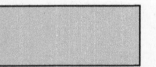

_____

6. **Stretch Your Thinking** Name the same activity you
might do at 9:00 A.M. and at 9:00 P.M.

_____

Homework

Write the time on the digital clocks.

1.

2.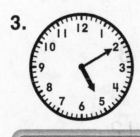

3.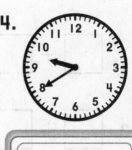

4.

Draw hands on each clock to show the time.

5.

8:15

6.

11:20

7.

12:30

8.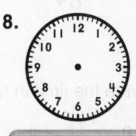

1:45

For each activity, ring the appropriate time.

9. trip to the zoo

   11:10 A.M.

   11:10 P.M.

10. building sand castles

   10:00 A.M.

   10:00 P.M.

11. bedtime story

   8:15 A.M.

   8:15 P.M.

12. shadow puppets

   9:30 A.M.

   9:30 P.M.

Remembering

Complete the addition doubles equation.

1. ☐ + ☐ = 8

2. ☐ + ☐ = 18

3. ☐ + ☐ = 12

4. ☐ + ☐ = 16

Add. Use any method.

5. 53
  + 89

6. 72
  + 48

7. 95
  + 66

Write the time in two different ways.

8.

_____ o'clock

9.

_____ o'clock

10.

_____ o'clock

11. **Stretch Your Thinking** Name three different times when both hands are between the 12 and the 3 on the clock.

_____

Homework

Use the picture graph to answer the questions.

Book Sales

Peter	📘	📘	📘	📘	📘					
Tammy	📘	📘	📘	📘						
Shana	📘	📘	📘	📘	📘	📘	📘	📘	📘	

1. Who sold the most books? _____

2. Who sold the fewest books? _____

3. How many more books did Shana sell than Tammy?

   ☐ _____

          label

4. How many fewer books did Peter sell than Shana?

   ☐ _____

          label

5. How many more books did Peter sell than Tammy?

   ☐ _____

          label

6. How many books did the children sell altogether?

   ☐ _____

          label

7. **Write Your Own** Write and solve your own question about the graph.

   _____

   _____

Remembering

Add ones or tens.

1. $5 + 9 = $ ☐ $4 + 7 = $ ☐ $6 + 7 = $ ☐

   $50 + 90 = $ ☐ $40 + 70 = $ ☐ $60 + 70 = $ ☐

Solve the word problem. Rewrite the 100 or make
a drawing. Add to check your work.

2. Savanna had 100 pennies in a jar. She spent some
   of them. She has 27 in the jar now. How many
   pennies did she spend?

   ☐ _____
        label

Draw hands on each clock to show the time.

3.    4.    5.    6.

   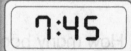

5:10   **2:50**   **10:25**   **7:45**

7. **Stretch Your Thinking** Without counting, how can
   you tell which item has the most on a picture graph?

   _____

   _____

Discuss Picture Graphs

Name _____

Homework

Read the picture graph.
Write the number. Ring *more* or *fewer*.

Number of Goldfish

Mina	🐟 🐟 🐟 🐟
Emily	🐟 🐟 🐟 🐟 🐟 🐟 🐟
Raj	🐟 🐟 🐟 🐟 🐟

1. Mina has [ ] *more* *fewer* goldfish than Emily.

2. Raj needs [ ] *more* *fewer* fish to have as many as Emily has.

Solve.

Number of Bells

Dan	🔔 🔔 🔔 🔔 🔔 🔔 🔔 🔔
Tani	🔔 🔔 🔔
Loren	🔔 🔔 🔔 🔔 🔔 🔔

3. How many bells do the children have altogether?

[ ] _____
　　　label

4. Dan has 6 red bells. The rest are yellow. How many of Dan's bells are yellow?

[ ] _____
　　　label

Remembering

Add in any order. Write the total.

1. $1 + 5 + 9 =$ ☐

2. $6 + 6 + 5 =$ ☐

3. $2 + 4 + 3 + 3 =$ ☐

4. $3 + 8 + 5 + 7 =$ ☐

Use the picture graph to answer the questions.

Pens

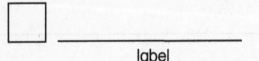

5. Who has the most pens? _____

6. Who has the fewest pens? _____

7. How many more pens does Sophia have
   than David?

   ☐ _____

          label

8. **Stretch Your Thinking** Without counting all of the
   pens, explain how you can find how many fewer pens
   Jeremy has than David.

   _____

   _____

   _____

Read Picture Graphs

Homework

1. The park has 9 oak trees, 2 maple trees, and 6 elm trees in it. Complete the data table.

Trees in the Park

Oak	
Maple	
Elm	

2. Use the data table to complete the bar graph.

Trees in the Park

Oak										
Maple										
Elm										

0 1 2 3 4 5 6 7 8 9 10

Use your bar graph. Write the number and ring *more* or *fewer*.

3. There are ☐ *more fewer* oak trees than maple trees in the park.

4. There are ☐ *more fewer* maple trees than elm trees in the park.

5. We need to plant ☐ *more fewer* elm trees to have as many elm trees as oak trees.

Remembering

Add.

1. $20 + 40 =$ _____ $10 + 90 =$ _____ $50 + 30 =$ _____

    $2 + 4 =$ _____ $1 + 9 =$ _____ $5 + 3 =$ _____

Read the picture graph.

Write the number. Ring *more* or *fewer*.

Number of Crayons

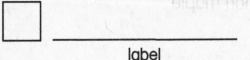

Ellen	✏ ✏ ✏ ✏
Brad	✏ ✏ ✏ ✏ ✏ ✏
Yoko	✏ ✏ ✏ ✏ ✏ ✏ ✏ ✏ ✏

2. Brad has [   ] *more fewer* crayons than Yoko.

3. Ellen needs [   ] *more fewer* crayons to have

as many crayons as Brad.

4. Five of Yoko's crayons are new. The rest of
her crayons are old. How many are old?

[   ] _____
       label

5. **Stretch Your Thinking** Explain how a bar graph
and a picture graph are alike.

_____

_____

_____

    Introduce Bar Graphs

Homework

Nineteen children each play a musical instrument.

Instruments Children Play

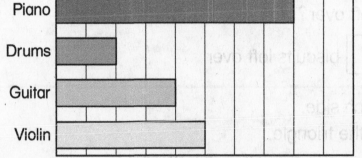

Use the bar graph to complete the sentences.

1. Two fewer children play the _____ than the guitar.

2. Nine children play the _____

   or the _____.

3. [ ] more children have to play the guitar to have
   the same number as the children who play the piano.

4. [ ] fewer children play the violin than play the piano.

5. [ ] children play the piano or the drums.

6. [ ] children play the piano, the guitar, or the violin.

Remembering

Solve. Make a proof drawing.   **Show your work.**

1. Megan bakes 57 biscuits. Each bag holds
   10 biscuits. How many bags will be full?
   How many biscuits will be left over?

   ☐ bags   ☐ biscuits left over

Estimate and then measure each side.
Then find the distance around the triangle.

2.

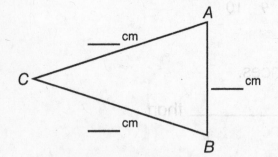

a. Complete the table.

Side	Estimate	Measure
AB		
BC		
CA		

b. Find the distance around the triangle.

_____ cm + _____ cm + _____ cm = _____ cm

---

3. Nathan has 6 cars, 4 trucks, and
   8 buses in his toy garage.
   Complete the table to show this.

   Nathan's Garage

Cars	
Trucks	
Buses	

4. **Stretch Your Thinking** Look at the completed table
   in Exercise 3. Explain how the bars would look if the
   information were in a bar graph.

   _____

   _____

     Read Bar Graphs

Use the bar graph to answer the questions below.
Fill in the circle next to the correct answer.

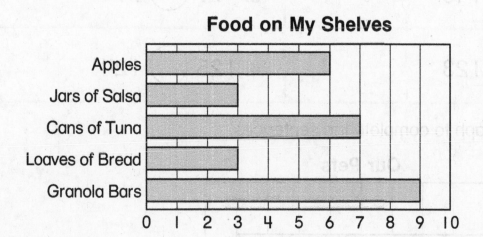

Food on My Shelves

Apples	
Jars of Salsa	
Cans of Tuna	
Loaves of Bread	
Granola Bars	

0 1 2 3 4 5 6 7 8 9 10

1. How many more cans of tuna are there than jars of salsa?

◯ 4
◯ 5
◯ 6
◯ 7

2. Altogether, how many apples and granola bars do I have?

◯ 11
◯ 13
◯ 15
◯ 16

3. I eat some apples. Now there are only 4 apples left. How many apples did I eat?

◯ 0
◯ 1
◯ 2
◯ 4

4. Write Your Own Write 1 question about the graph. Answer your question.

_____

_____

Remembering

Write <, >, or =.

1. 164 ◯ 146

2. 79 ◯ 79

3. 88 ◯ 123

4. 125 ◯ 124

Use the bar graph to complete the sentences.

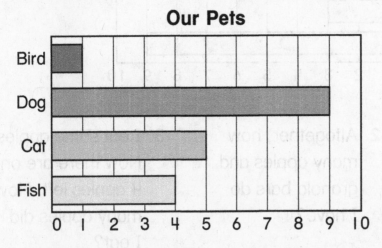

Our Pets

5. Three fewer children have _____ than fish.

6. Thirteen children have _____ or _____.

7. _____ more children need to have cats
to have the same number as the children who
have dogs.

8. **Stretch Your Thinking** Look at the bar graph.
Name three ways that the information could
change so that there would be the same number
of birds and cats.

_____

_____

Solve Problems Using a Bar Graphs

Homework

1. Prince won 8 medals at the dog show.
Lady won 5 medals. Muffy won 3 medals.
Make a table to show this.

_____

Dog	Medals

2. Use the information in the table to make a
picture graph. Use a circle for each 🏅.

_____

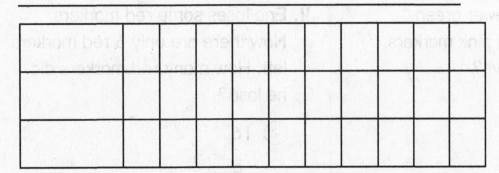

3. Use the information in the table to make a bar graph.

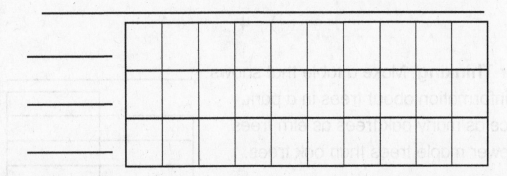

Remembering

Subtract using any method.

1. 73
  − 42
  _____

2. 60
  − 18
  _____

Use the bar graph to answer the questions below.
Fill in the circle next to the correct answer.

Eric's Markers

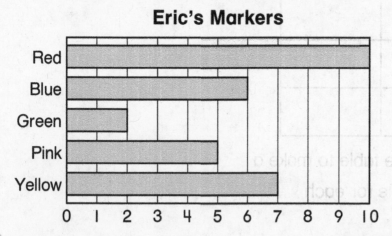

3. How many fewer green markers than pink markers does Eric have?

  ◯ 5
  ◯ 4
  ◯ 3
  ◯ 2

4. Eric loses some red markers. Now there are only 6 red markers left. How many red markers did he lose?

  ◯ 16
  ◯ 9
  ◯ 5
  ◯ 4

5. **Stretch Your Thinking** Make a table that shows the following information about trees in a park. There are twice as many oak trees as elm trees. There are 3 fewer maple trees than oak trees.

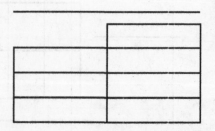

Collect and Graph Data

Homework

Books Read

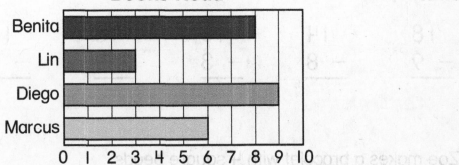

Use the bar graph to solve the problems.

1. Benita read 4 history books. The rest were science books. How many science books did she read?

⬜ _____
   label

2. Marcus read 3 fewer books than Gina. How many books did Gina read?

⬜ _____
   label

3. Diego read 4 more books than Eva. How many books did Eva read?

⬜ _____
   label

4. How many more books did Marcus and Diego read than Benita and Lin?

⬜ _____
   label

5. Ali read 4 more books than Lin and Marcus. How many books did Ali read?

⬜ _____
   label

Remembering

Subtract.

1. $\begin{array}{r} 18 \\ -9 \\ \hline \end{array}$ $\qquad$ $\begin{array}{r} 14 \\ -8 \\ \hline \end{array}$ $\qquad$ $\begin{array}{r} 10 \\ -3 \\ \hline \end{array}$ $\qquad$ $\begin{array}{r} 15 \\ -9 \\ \hline \end{array}$ $\qquad$ $\begin{array}{r} 16 \\ -7 \\ \hline \end{array}$ $\qquad$ $\begin{array}{r} 11 \\ -5 \\ \hline \end{array}$

2. Zoe makes a bracelet with 4 square beads,
   1 oval bead, and 9 heart beads. Make a table
   to show this.

   _____

3. Use the information in the table to make a picture
   graph. Use a circle for each bead.

   _____

   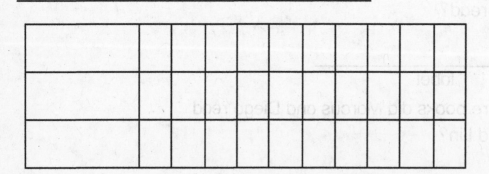

4. **Stretch Your Thinking** Tell something the
   graph shows.

   _____

   _____

Make Graphs and Interpret Data

Homework

Ms. Morgan asked the children in her class which
of these pets they liked best.

Which Is Your Favorite Pet?

Dog	O O O O O O O O O
Cat	O O O O O O
Bird	O O O O
Fish	O O O O O

1. Use the information in the table to make a bar graph.

Title: _____

_____

2. Think about your favorite pet. How would the graph change
if you added your own answer to the question?

_____

_____

Name _____

Remembering

Write how to count the money.

1.

<u>25¢</u>　　<u>35¢</u>　　____　____　____　____　____

Use the bar graph to solve the problems.

Crayons in Box

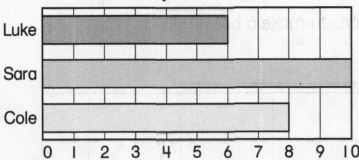

Luke

Sara

Cole

0　1　2　3　4　5　6　7　8　9　10

2. Five of Sara's crayons are new. The rest are old. How many crayons are old?

☐ _____

3. Alexa has 3 more crayons than Luke. How many crayons does Alexa have?

☐ _____

4. **Stretch Your Thinking** Look at the bar graph. Explain what could change so that everyone has the same number of crayons.

_____

_____

　　　　Focus on Mathematical Practices

Homework

Count the hundreds, tens, and ones.
Write the totals.

1. ☐ |||||| |||| ⚬⚬⚬⚬⚬ / ⚬⚬⚬

_____   _____   _____   Total _____
Hundreds   Tens   Ones

2. ☐ ☐ ☐ ☐ ||||| ⚬⚬⚬⚬⚬ / ⚬⚬⚬⚬

_____   _____   _____   Total _____
Hundreds   Tens   Ones

Draw to show the numbers. Use boxes, sticks, and circles.

3. __2__   __4__   __3__   4. __4__   __6__   __8__
Hundreds   Tens   Ones   Hundreds   Tens   Ones

5. __3__   __8__   __2__   6. __1__   __7__   __7__
Hundreds   Tens   Ones   Hundreds   Tens   Ones

Remembering

Add.

| 1. | 43
+ 28 | 2. | 65
+ 17 | 3. | 35
+ 28 | 4. | 52
+ 38 | 5. | 47
+ 29 |

Write <, >, or =.

6. 153 $\bigcirc$ 181   7. 113 $\bigcirc$ 131

8. 56 $\bigcirc$ 104   9. 59 $\bigcirc$ 59

10. 84 $\bigcirc$ 48   11. 151 $\bigcirc$ 139

12. Write how to count the money.

25¢ ___ ___ ___ ___ ___ ___ ___

13. **Stretch Your Thinking** You have base ten blocks for 2 hundreds, 2 tens, and 2 ones. Write all of the different 3-digit numbers you could show.

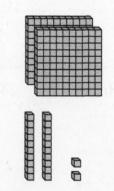

_____

_____

Homework

Write the hundreds, tens, and ones.

1. $675 =$ __600__ $+$ __70__ $+$ __5__
   H T O

2. $519 =$ _____ $+$ _____ $+$ _____

3. $831 =$ _____ $+$ _____ $+$ _____

4. $487 =$ _____ $+$ _____ $+$ _____

5. $222 =$ _____ $+$ _____ $+$ _____

6. $765 =$ _____ $+$ _____ $+$ _____

Write the number.

7. $300 + 40 + 6 =$ __346__
                    H T O

8. $100 + 60 \quad =$ _____

9. $700 + \quad 4 =$ _____

10. $200 + 50 + 3 =$ _____

11. $400 + 70 + 1 =$ _____

12. $800 + 80 + 8 =$ _____

Write the number that makes the equation true.

13. _____ $= 30 + 5 + 400$

14. $2 + 80 + 600 =$ _____

15. _____ $= 60 + 800$

16. $900 + 7 + 40 =$ _____

17. _____ $= 300 + 4 + 50$

18. $1 + 500 \quad =$ _____

19. $729 = 20 + 9 +$ _____

20. _____ $+ 6 + 200 = 296$

Name _____

Remembering

Add in any order. Write the total.

1. $8 + 1 + 4 =$ ☐

2. $6 + 9 + 5 =$ ☐

3. $7 + 4 + 3 =$ ☐

4. $8 + 3 + 2 =$ ☐

Draw a Math Mountain to solve the word problem.   **Show your work.**
Show how you add or subtract.

5. There are 23 girls and 49 boys
standing in line. How many
children are standing in line?

☐ _____
   label

6. Count the hundreds, tens, and ones.
Write the total.

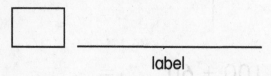

___ ___   ___   Total ___
Hundreds   Tens   Ones

7. Stretch Your Thinking Write an addition equation.
The equation must have a 1-, a 2-, and a 3-digit
addend and use all of these digits.

6   6   2   2   8   8   0   0   0

_____

_____

Place Value

Homework

Write <, >, or =.

1. 285 ◯ 385

2. 452 ◯ 425

3. 961 ◯ 691

4. 199 ◯ 205

5. 754 ◯ 861

6. 738 ◯ 694

7. 367 ◯ 67

8. 274 ◯ 274

9. 158 ◯ 159

10. 106 ◯ 99

11. 222 ◯ 333

12. 73 ◯ 511

13. 604 ◯ 604

14. 138 ◯ 136

15. 288 ◯ 386

16. 207 ◯ 197

17. 648 ◯ 734

18. 549 ◯ 559

19. 762 ◯ 643

20. 709 ◯ 810

21. 691 ◯ 961

22. 802 ◯ 802

Remembering

Be the helper. Is the answer OK? Write *yes* or *no*.
If *no*, fix the mistakes and write the correct answer.

1. 28
    + 34
    ─────
    62   OK? ☐

2. 58
    + 17
    ─────
    515   OK? ☐

3. 45
    + 26
    ─────
    61   OK? ☐

Add up to solve the word problem.   **Show your work.**

4. Allison has 67 beads. She uses some beads to
   make a necklace. Now she has 39 beads. How
   many beads did Allison use for her necklace?

   ☐ _____
        label

Write the number.

5. 400 + 10 + 5 = _____   6. 800 + 7 = _____

7. **Stretch Your Thinking** Use the digits to write pairs of 3-digit numbers.
   Write <, >, or = to compare the pairs of numbers you write.

             6   1   3   7   2   0

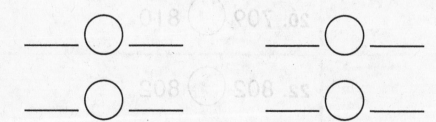

Compare Numbers

Homework

Count by ones. Write the numbers.

1. 396 397 __398__ __399__ __400__ __401__ __402__ __403__ 404

2. 695 696 ___ ___ ___ ___ ___ ___ 703

3. 498 499 ___ ___ ___ ___ ___ ___ 506

4. 894 ___ ___ ___ ___ ___ ___ ___ 902

5. 796 ___ ___ ___ ___ ___ ___ ___ 804

Count by tens. Write the numbers.

6. 830 840 __850__ __860__ __870__ __880__ __890__ __900__ 910

7. 470 480 ___ ___ ___ ___ ___ 550

8. 740 ___ ___ ___ ___ ___ ___ 820

9. 380 ___ ___ ___ ___ ___ ___ 460

10. 560 ___ ___ ___ ___ ___ ___ 640

Write the number name.

11. 597 _____

12. 640 _____

Remembering

Find the total or partner.

1.
$\begin{array}{r} 4 \\ + 8 \\ \hline \end{array}$
$\begin{array}{r} 9 \\ + 6 \\ \hline \end{array}$
$\begin{array}{r} 7 \\ + 5 \\ \hline \end{array}$
$\begin{array}{r} 13 \\ - 7 \\ \hline \end{array}$
$\begin{array}{r} 16 \\ - 9 \\ \hline \end{array}$
$\begin{array}{r} 18 \\ - 9 \\ \hline \end{array}$

Solve the word problem.   **Show your work.**

2. Cameron reads 57 pages on Monday and
   85 pages on Tuesday. How many pages
   does he read in all?

   _____
            label

Write <. >, or =.

3. 675 $\bigcirc$ 657   4. 198 $\bigcirc$ 201

5. 86 $\bigcirc$ 124   6. 36 $\bigcirc$ 36

7. **Stretch Your Thinking** Natalie practices the piano
   every day. On Monday she practiced for 10 minutes.
   If she practices every day for 10 minutes, on which
   day of the week will she have practiced for
   90 minutes? Explain.

   _____

   _____

   _____

Count by Ones and by Tens

Homework

Solve each word problem.

1. Maria blows up some balloons for a party. She divides them into 4 groups of one hundred and 7 groups of ten. There are 6 balloons left over. How many balloons does Maria blow up for the party?

2. Roger has 5 erasers. He buys 6 packages of one hundred and 2 packages of ten. How many erasers does Roger have altogether?

[ ] _____
label

[ ] _____
label

3. Add.

$400 + 200 = $ ____	$440 + 7 = $ ____	$16 + 700 = $ ____
$40 + 50 = $ ____	$84 + 10 = $ ____	$70 + 7 = $ ____
$8 + 460 = $ ____	$200 + 9 = $ ____	$53 + 500 = $ ____
$30 + 10 = $ ____	$60 + 40 = $ ____	$60 + 4 = $ ____
$380 + 10 = $ ____	$900 + 80 = $ ____	$800 + 200 = $ ____

Name _____

Remembering

Look for shapes around you.

1. List or draw objects that show rectangles.

Solve the word problem. Draw a
proof drawing if you need to.

Show your work.

2. There are 200 people with tickets for the
Fall Festival. A worker collects tickets
from 62 of the people. How many tickets
are still left to collect?

[   ] _____
label

Count by tens. Write the numbers.

3. 650 660 _____ _____ _____ _____ _____ _____ 730

4. Stretch Your Thinking Brian has some boxes of
paper clips. Some boxes hold 10 clips and some
boxes hold 100. He has some paper clips left over.
He has three more boxes with 100 paper clips than
he has boxes with 10 paper clips. He has two fewer
paper clips left over than he has numbers of boxes
with 100 paper clips. What number of paper clips
could he have?

_____

Add Ones, Tens, and Hundreds

Homework

Solve each word problem.

1. Martin sells 58 tickets to the roller coaster ride. He sells 267 tickets to the boat ride. How many tickets does Martin sell altogether?

2. Justine jumps 485 times on a pogo stick. Then she jumps 329 times when she tries again. How many times does she jump altogether?

[   ] _____
label

[   ] _____
label

Add.

3. $18 + 549 =$ [   ]

4. $190 + 89 =$ [   ]

5. $76 + 570 =$ [   ]

6. $75 + 656 =$ [   ]

7. $348 + 162 =$ [   ]

8. $407 + 394 =$ [   ]

Name _____

Remembering

Add. Use any method.

1. 53
   + 39
   ‾‾‾‾

2. 45
   + 86
   ‾‾‾‾

3. 75
   + 68
   ‾‾‾‾

Label the shapes using the words in the box.

| cube | quadrilateral | pentagon | hexagon |

4.
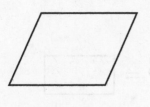
_____

5.
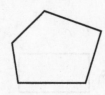
_____

Add.

6. $300 + 70 =$ _____ $20 + 40 =$ _____ $8 + 650 =$ _____

7. **Stretch Your Thinking** Add a 3-digit number
   and a 2-digit number. Use the digits 5, 6, 7,
   and 8 to write the addition exercise. You can
   use a digit more than once. Find the sum.

   _____

© Houghton Mifflin Harcourt Publishing Company

Homework

Add. Use any method.

1.   459
     + 267

Make a new ten?   _____

Make a new hundred?   _____

Make a new thousand? _____

2. 187 + 374 = _____

Make a new ten?   _____

Make a new hundred?   _____

Make a new thousand? _____

3.   678
     + 15

Make a new ten?   _____

Make a new hundred?   _____

Make a new thousand? _____

4. 635 + 92 = _____

Make a new ten?   _____

Make a new hundred?   _____

Make a new thousand? _____

5.   390
     + 610

Make a new ten?   _____

Make a new hundred?   _____

Make a new thousand? _____

6. 64 + 936 = _____

Make a new ten?   _____

Make a new hundred?   _____

Make a new thousand? _____

Name _____

Remembering

Measure each vertical line segment below by
marking and counting 1-cm lengths.

1. | **2.** | **3.**

[ ] cm   [ ] cm   [ ] cm

Solve the word problem.

4. A man sells 275 circus tickets on Monday
morning and 369 circus tickets on Monday
afternoon. How many tickets does he
sell on Monday?

[ ] _____
label

5. Stretch Your Thinking Write an addition exercise
with a sum of 1,000. Use two 3-digit addends. Choose
addends so that you will need to make a new ten,
a new hundred, and a new thousand when you add.

_____

_____

Discuss 3-Digit Addition

Solve each word problem.   **Show your work.**

1. Angie has 648 stickers. 254 of the stickers
   are cat stickers. The rest are dog stickers.
   How many dog stickers does Angie have?

   ☐ _____
              label

2. Billy has 315 coins. 209 of the coins are
   silver in color. How many coins are not
   silver in color?

   ☐ _____
              label

3. Noah is going to plant 752 seeds. Some
   of the seeds are flower seeds. 547 of the
   seeds are vegetable seeds. How many
   flower seeds will Noah plant?

   ☐ _____
              label

4. Heather's dad is reading a book that is 564
   pages long. So far he has read 286 pages.
   How many pages does he have left to read?

   ☐ _____
              label

Remembering

Make a ten to find the total.

1. $7 + 6 = \boxed{}$ **2.** $8 + 7 = \boxed{}$ **3.** $8 + 9 = \boxed{}$

Write the time in two different ways.

4.

_____ o'clock

5.

_____ o'clock

6.

_____ o'clock

Add. Use any method.

7.   357
       + 585

8. $249 + 751 = $ _____

Make a new ten? _____	Make a new ten? _____
Make a new hundred? _____	Make a new hundred? _____
Make a new thousand? _____	Make a new thousand? _____

9. Stretch Your Thinking Explain how to solve for an unknown addend.

_____

_____

Word Problems: Unknown Addends

Homework

Solve the word problems. Use your favorite
method. Make a proof drawing.

1. Ricardo likes olives. He has
100 olives. He eats 43 of them.
How many olives does he have
left?

_____ _____
                 label

2. Dawn has 1,000 pennies in her
penny jar. She gives some to her
sister. Now she has 432 left. How
many pennies does Dawn give to
her sister?

_____ _____
                 label

3. Tory sells hockey sticks to teams
in her city. She has 500 and sells
353. How many hockey sticks
does she have left to sell?

_____ _____
                 label

4. Randy collects magnets. Over
two years he collects 400 magnets.
He collects 125 magnets the first
year. How many does he collect
the second year?

_____ _____
                 label

Remembering

Add.

1.   5 + 6 = _____   7 + 9 = _____   100 + 35 = _____

    50 + 60 = _____   70 + 90 = _____   10 + 35 = _____

                                                    1 + 35 = _____

Draw hands on each clock to show the time.

2.    3.    4.    5.

4:10   1:30   7:15   10:45

Solve the word problem.

6. The school has 537 children. 359 of the children had
   lunch. How many children still need to have lunch?

    _____
        label

7. **Stretch Your Thinking** How is subtracting from
   a 3-digit number different from subtracting from a
   2-digit number?

   _____

   _____

   _____

Subtract from Hundreds Numbers

Decide if you need to ungroup. If you need to ungroup, draw a magnifying glass around the top number. Then find the answer.

1.   730
   − 499
   _____

Ungroup to get 10 ones? _____

Ungroup to get 10 tens? _____

2.   950
   − 639
   _____

Ungroup to get 10 ones? _____

Ungroup to get 10 tens? _____

3.   300
   − 167
   _____

Ungroup to get 10 ones? _____

Ungroup to get 10 tens? _____

4.   404
   − 188
   _____

Ungroup to get 10 ones? _____

Ungroup to get 10 tens? _____

5.   420
   − 183
   _____

Ungroup to get 10 ones? _____

Ungroup to get 10 tens? _____

6. 502 − 149 = _____

Ungroup to get 10 ones? _____

Ungroup to get 10 tens? _____

Name _____

Remembering

Use the picture graph to answer the questions.

Crayons

Paige	✏	✏	✏	✏	✏	✏	✏	✏
Tawana	✏	✏						
Colin	✏	✏	✏	✏	✏			

1. Who has the most crayons? _____

2. Who has the fewest crayons? _____

3. How many crayons do they all have together?

[ ] _____

label

Solve the word problem. Use your favorite method.
Make a proof drawing.

4. There are 500 craft sticks in the box.
The art class uses 386 of the craft sticks.
How many craft sticks are left?

[ ] _____

label

---

5. Stretch Your Thinking When you are subtracting
from a 3-digit number, how do you know if you will
need to ungroup?

_____

_____

Subtract from Numbers with Zeros

Name _____

Homework

Decide if you need to ungroup. If you need to ungroup,
draw a magnifying glass around the top number.
Then find the answer.

1.
$$\begin{array}{r} 5\ 3\ 1 \\ -\ 4\ 3\ 4 \\ \hline \end{array}$$

Ungroup to get 10 ones? _____

Ungroup to get 10 tens? _____

2.
$$\begin{array}{r} 5\ 7\ 9 \\ -\ 2\ 9\ 6 \\ \hline \end{array}$$

Ungroup to get 10 ones? _____

Ungroup to get 10 tens? _____

3.
$$\begin{array}{r} 3\ 9\ 1 \\ -\ 2\ 6\ 5 \\ \hline \end{array}$$

Ungroup to get 10 ones? _____

Ungroup to get 10 tens? _____

4. $238 - 177 =$ _____

Ungroup to get 10 ones? _____

Ungroup to get 10 tens? _____

5. Latoya's class picks 572 apples on
a field trip. They bring 386 apples
home with them. How many apples
do they leave?

[_____]
_____ label

6. Elena had 735 stickers. She gives
427 stickers to her brother. How
many stickers does she have left?

[_____]
_____ label

Remembering

Subtract.

1. $\begin{array}{r} 61 \\ -\ 25 \\ \hline \end{array}$
2. $\begin{array}{r} 85 \\ -\ 34 \\ \hline \end{array}$
3. $\begin{array}{r} 93 \\ -\ 24 \\ \hline \end{array}$
4. $\begin{array}{r} 52 \\ -\ 23 \\ \hline \end{array}$
5. $\begin{array}{r} 91 \\ -\ 54 \\ \hline \end{array}$

Read the picture graph.
Write the number. Ring *more* or *fewer*.

Number of Marbles

Ling	🔵 🔵 🔵 🔵 🔵
Sean	🔵 🔵 🔵 🔵 🔵 🔵 🔵 🔵 🔵 🔵
Maya	🔵 🔵 🔵 🔵 🔵 🔵 🔵

6. Sean has ☐ *more fewer* marbles than Ling.

7. Maya needs ☐ *more fewer* marbles to have as many

marbles as Sean.

Decide if you need to ungroup. If you need to ungroup,
draw a magnifying glass around the top number. Then
find the answer.

8. $\begin{array}{r} 863 \\ -\ 245 \\ \hline \end{array}$

Ungroup to get 10 ones? _____

Ungroup to get 10 tens? _____

9. **Stretch Your Thinking** Write and solve a subtraction
exercise in which you need to ungroup two times.

Subtract from Any 3-Digit Number

Decide if you need to ungroup. If you need to ungroup, draw a magnifying glass around the top number. Then find the answer.

1.
```
  6 3 0
– 3 1 8
```

Ungroup to get 10 ones? _____

Ungroup to get 10 tens? _____

2.
```
  9 3 1
– 8 4 5
```

Ungroup to get 10 ones? _____

Ungroup to get 10 tens? _____

3.
```
  4 0 7
– 2 7 4
```

Ungroup to get 10 ones? _____

Ungroup to get 10 tens? _____

4.
```
  4 9 8
– 2 7 6
```

Ungroup to get 10 ones? _____

Ungroup to get 10 tens? _____

5. Jamal has 590 craft sticks. He uses 413 craft sticks to make a building. How many craft sticks does he have left?

[   ] _____
          label

6. On Saturday, 290 people go to the roller skating rink. 184 of them are adults. How many are children?

[   ] _____
          label

Name _____

Remembering

Under each picture, write the total amount of
money so far. Then write the total using $.

1.   100¢   25¢   1¢   1¢

_____   _____   _____   _____ $ ___.___ ___
                                                                total

Make a drawing. Write an equation. Solve.

2. Jiao has some beads. Then she buys
35 more beads. Now she has 73 beads.
How many beads did Jiao start with?

[   ] _____
          label

Decide if you need to ungroup. If you need
to ungroup, draw a magnifying glass around
the top number. Then find the answer.

3.   5 3 7   Ungroup to get 10 ones? _____

    – 1 6 8   Ungroup to get 10 tens? _____

4. Stretch Your Thinking What 3-digit number
would need no ungrouping to subtract from? Explain.

_____

_____

                        Practice Ungrouping

Name _____

Homework

Decide if you need to add or subtract. Use the
opposite operation to check your answer.

1.
```
   184
 + 433
```

2.
```
   552
 - 399
```

3.
```
   328
 - 119
```

4.
```
   288
 + 294
```

5. 967 − 548 = _____

6. 474 − 355 = _____

Remembering

Use the bar graph to complete the sentences.

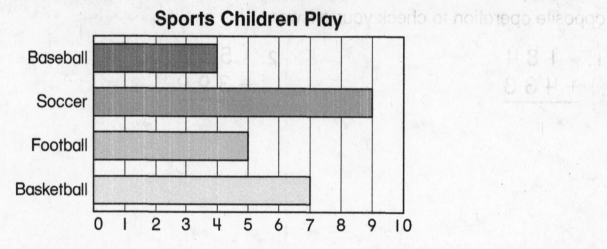

Sports Children Play

1. Four fewer children play _____ than soccer.

2. Eleven children play _____ or _____.

Decide if you need to ungroup. If you need to ungroup,
draw a magnifying glass around the top number. Then
find the answer.

3.   427   Ungroup to get 10 ones? _____
    − 159   Ungroup to get 10 tens? _____

4. **Stretch Your Thinking** Explain why you
can check subtraction by adding.

_____

_____

_____

Homework

Solve each word problem.

1. Mario buys 98 plastic cups. He gives 29 to the art teacher. How many cups does he have left?

2. Joel collects baseball cards. He has 568 cards. Then he buys 329 more at a yard sale. How many cards does he have now?

label

label

3. A bird collects 392 sticks to build a nest. Then the bird collects 165 more. How many sticks does the bird collect?

4. There are 765 books in the school library. 259 are paperback, and the rest are hardcover. How many hardcover books are there in the school library?

label

label

Remembering

Make a drawing. Write an equation. Solve the problem.

1. There are some children in the class.
   8 are girls and 9 are boys. How many
   children are in the class?

   ┌─────┐　_____
   │   │
   └─────┘
   　　　　　　　　label

Estimate and then measure each side.
Then find the distance around the triangle.

2.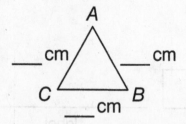

a. Complete the table.

Side	Estimate	Measure
AB		
BC		
CA		

b. Find the distance around the triangle.

_____ cm + _____ cm + _____ cm = _____ cm

Decide if you need to add or subtract. Use the
opposite operation to check your answer.

3. 　6 8 3　　　　　　　　4. 　2 5 7
   − 1 4 5　　　　　　　　　 + 3 6 9

5. **Stretch Your Thinking** Write and solve a subtraction
   word problem with an answer greater than 500 pennies.

   _____

   _____

   _____

　　　　　Mixed Addition and Subtraction Word Problems

Homework

The table shows the number of children who take part in different after school activities.

Use the table to solve the word problems.

Show your work.

After School Activities	
Activity	**Number of Children**
Art Club	378
Music Lessons	205
Sports	204
Dance Class	105
Science Club	217

1. One hundred seventeen girls take music lessons after school. How many boys take music lessons?

   ☐ _____
   label

2. How many fewer children signed up for music and dance than signed up for the art club?

   ☐ _____
   label

3. Write a word problem using data from the table. Solve the problem.

   _____

   _____

   _____

Remembering

Estimate and then measure each side.
Then find the distance around the rectangle.

1.

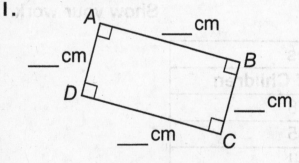

a. Complete the table.

Side	Estimate	Measure
AB		
BC		
CD		
DA		

b. Find the distance around the rectangle.

_____ cm + _____ cm + _____ cm + _____ cm = _____ cm

Solve the word problem.

2. The store has 374 CDs. A box with
258 CDs arrives at the store. How
many CDs does the store have now?

[   ] _____
          label

3. Stretch Your Thinking Fill in the digits to
complete the addition exercise.

$$\begin{array}{r} 1\ \square\ 4 \\ +\ \square\ 6\ \square \\ \hline 4\ 5\ 1 \end{array}$$

Focus on Mathematical Practices

Write how many in each row and in each column.
Then write two equations for each array.

1.    ____
____
____
____
____

____ ____ ____ ____

_____

_____

2. 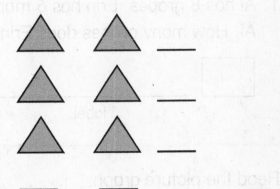   ____
____
____

____

_____

_____

Measure in centimeters. Draw rows and columns.
Write the number of small squares.

3.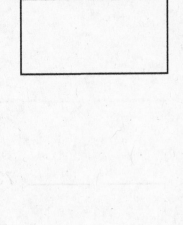

____ squares

4.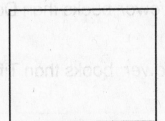

____ squares

5.

____ squares

Remembering

Make a matching drawing or draw comparison bars.
Solve the problem.

1. Al has 8 grapes. Erin has 6 more grapes than
   Al. How many grapes does Erin have?

   ☐   _____

            label

Read the picture graph.
Write the number. Ring *more* or *fewer*.

Number of Books

David	📖 📖 📖
Tiffany	📖 📖 📖 📖 📖 📖 📖 📖 📖
Pedro	📖 📖 📖 📖 📖 📖

2. Tiffany has ☐ *more* *fewer* books than David.

3. Pedro has ☐ *more* *fewer* books than Tiffany.

Count by tens. Write the numbers.

4. 650 ____ ____ ____ ____ ____ ____ 730

5. **Stretch Your Thinking** Draw three different
   arrays that show 12.

Homework

1. Make 2 halves. Show different ways.
   Shade half of each rectangle.

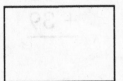  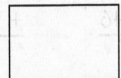 

2. Make 3 thirds. Show different ways.
   Shade a third of each rectangle.

3. Make 4 fourths. Show different ways.
   Shade a fourth of each rectangle.

4. Make 2 halves.
   Shade half of
   the circle.

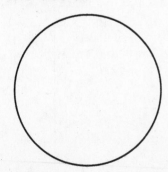

5. Make 3 thirds.
   Shade a third of
   the circle.

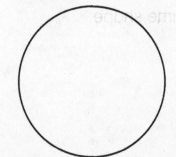

6. Make 4 fourths.
   Shade a fourth of
   the circle.

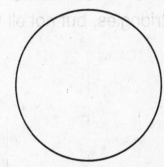

Remembering

Add.

1. 73
   +19
   _____

2. 53
   +46
   _____

3. 68
   +23
   _____

4. 27
   +35
   _____

5. 46
   +39
   _____

Write how many in each row and in each column.
Then write two equations for each array.

6.

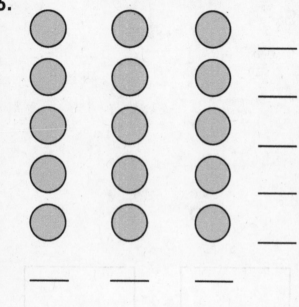

_____

_____

_____

_____

_____

___ ___ ___

_____

7.

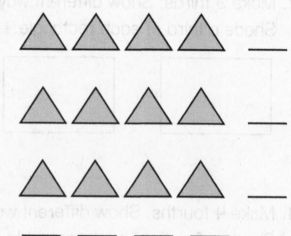

_____

_____

_____

_____

8. **Stretch Your Thinking** Draw a rectangle.
   Show 4 fourths that are all the same-size
   triangles, but not all the same shape.

Find Equal Shares

Name _____

Homework

Solve. **Show your work.**

1. Becky's garden is 21 meters wide.
Jerry's garden is 17 meters wide.
How much wider is Becky's garden
than Jerry's garden?

☐ _____
       unit

2. Hannah's painting is 39 inches long.
She adds 12 inches to it. How long
is the painting now?

☐ _____
       unit

Use the number line diagram to add or subtract.

3. Loop 28 and 56. Loop the difference D.

How long is it? _____

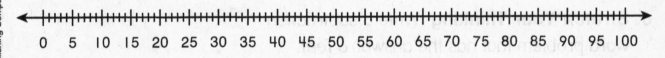

4. Loop 48. Add 15 to it. Loop the total T.

How long is it? _____

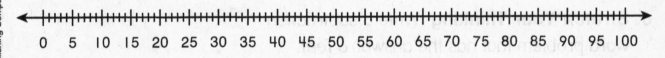

Remembering

Add.

1. $14 + 46 + 62 + 39 =$ [   ]

2. Count the hundreds, tens, and ones.

   Write the total.

   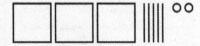

   _____   _____   _____   Total _____
   Hundreds   **Tens**   **Ones**

3. Make 2 halves.

4. Make 3 thirds.

   [   ]

5. Make 4 fourths.

   [   ]

6. **Stretch Your Thinking** Write a subtraction word problem that has the answer *6 feet*.

   _____

   _____

   _____

Homework

Solve. Show your work.

1. Here is the path Fluffy took on her walk today. How many meters did she walk?

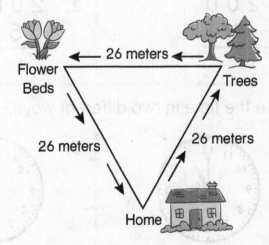

_____
unit

2. Colin wants to decorate a picture frame with gold ribbon. How long should the ribbon be if he wants to put ribbon around the whole frame?

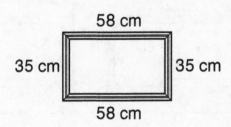

_____
unit

3. Here is a top view drawing of the new sandbox for the park. Each side is 16 feet long. A border runs along the edge. How long is the border?

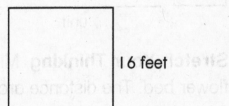

_____
unit

Remembering

Subtract.

1.	2 0 0 − 4 1	2.	2 0 0 − 5 5	3.	2 0 0 − 8 7

Write the time in two different ways.

4. 	5. 	6. 
_____ o'clock	_____ o'clock	_____ o'clock
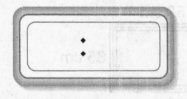	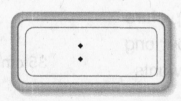	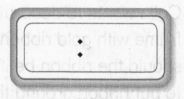

Solve.   **Show your work.**

7. Jen's paper is 30 cm long. She cuts
   12 cm from the bottom of the paper.
   How long is her paper now?

   [   ] _____
          unit

8. **Stretch Your Thinking** Michael has a triangle-shaped
   flower bed. The distance around the flower bed is
   58 feet. What could be the length of each side?

   _____

   _____

Add Three and Four Lengths

Name _____

Homework

Represent each equation on the number line diagram.
Then find the difference or the total.

1. 56 + ☐ = 94

0 5 10 15 20 25 30 35 40 45 50 55 60 65 70 75 80 85 90 95 100

2. 34 + 47 = ☐

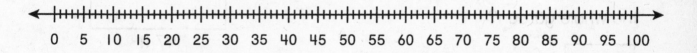

0 5 10 15 20 25 30 35 40 45 50 55 60 65 70 75 80 85 90 95 100

3. ☐ + 31 = 69

0 5 10 15 20 25 30 35 40 45 50 55 60 65 70 75 80 85 90 95 100

4. 42 + 29 = ☐

0 5 10 15 20 25 30 35 40 45 50 55 60 65 70 75 80 85 90 95 100

Remembering

Solve. Rewrite the 100 or make a drawing.   **Show your work.**
Add to check your answer.

1. Brian sees 100 cars in the parking lot.
36 of the cars leave. How many cars
are still in the parking lot?

┌─────────┐
│   │ _____
└─────────┘   label

Solve.

2. Mr. Kensey is putting a fence around
his garden. How much fencing will he
need if he wants to put a fence around
the whole garden?

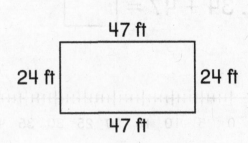

┌─────────┐
│   │ _____
└─────────┘   unit

---

3. Stretch Your Thinking What equation is
shown by this number line?

_____

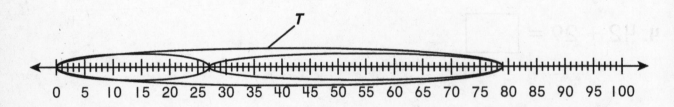

Homework

1. Show 2 halves.

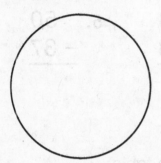

2. Show 3 thirds.

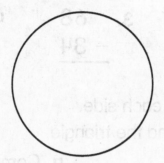

3. Show 4 fourths.

Roberto, Niko, and Maya each buy a pizza.
All their pizzas are the same size.

- Roberto cuts his pizza into 2 equal parts.

- Niko cuts his pizza into 3 equal parts.

- Maya cuts her pizza into 4 equal parts.

4. Roberto eats 2 halves and Maya eats 4 fourths.
Do they eat the same amount? Explain.

_____

_____

_____

5. Is half of Roberto's pizza greater than, less than,
or equal to a third of Maya's pizza? Explain.

_____

_____

_____

Remembering

Subtract.

1. 73	2. 91	3. 68	4. 83	5. 50
− 45	− 37	− 34	− 18	− 37

Estimate and then measure each side.
Then find the distance around the triangle.

6.

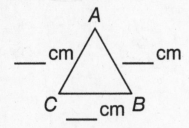

a. Complete the table.

Side	Estimate	Measure
AB		
BC		
CA		

b. Find the distance around the triangle.

_____ cm + _____ cm + _____ cm = _____ cm

Show the equation on the number line diagram.
Then find the difference or the total.

7. $35 + \boxed{} = 78$

⟵ |┼┼┼|┼┼┼|┼┼┼|┼┼┼|┼┼┼|┼┼┼|┼┼┼|┼┼┼|┼┼┼|┼┼┼|┼┼┼|┼┼┼|┼┼┼|┼┼┼|┼┼┼|┼┼┼|┼┼┼|┼┼┼|┼┼┼|┼┼┼| ⟶

0 5 10 15 20 25 30 35 40 45 50 55 60 65 70 75 80 85 90 95 100

8. **Stretch Your Thinking** Dennis and Tami each make a
pizza. Both pizzas are the same size and shape. Dennis
eats 4 pieces. Tami eats 2 pieces. Could they each have
eaten the same amount? Explain.

_____

_____